# COLLECTIONS
# FOR YOUNG SCHOLARS™
### VOLUME 3   BOOK I

*Friendship*

*Imagination*

*Money*

Art by Marcy Ramsey

# COLLECTIONS FOR YOUNG SCHOLARS™

VOLUME 3  BOOK I

PROGRAM AUTHORS
*Carl Bereiter*
*Ann Brown*
*Marlene Scardamalia*
*Joe Campione*
*Valerie Anderson*

CONSULTING AUTHORS
*Michael Pressley*
*Iva Carruthers*
*Bill Pinkney*

OPEN COURT PUBLISHING COMPANY
CHICAGO AND PERU, ILLINOIS

CHAIRMAN
M. Blouke Carus

PRESIDENT
André W. Carus

EDUCATION DIRECTOR
Carl Bereiter

CONCEPT
Barbara Conteh

EXECUTIVE EDITOR
Shirley Graudin

MANAGING EDITOR
Sheelagh McGurn

SENIOR PROJECT EDITOR
Theresa Kryst Fertig

ART DIRECTOR
John Grandits

VICE-PRESIDENT, PRODUCTION
AND MANUFACTURING
Chris Vancalbergh

PERMISSIONS COORDINATOR
Diane Sikora

COVER ARTIST
Marcy Ramsey

4

Printed in the United States of America

ISBN 0-8126-3148-X

10 9 8 7 6 5 4 3

# ACKNOWLEDGMENTS

Grateful acknowledgment is given to the following publishers and copyright owners for permission granted to reprint selections from their publications. All possible care has been taken to trace ownership and secure permission for each selection included.

Atheneum Publishers, an imprint of Macmillan, Inc.: *Alexander Who Used to Be Rich Last Sunday* by Judith Viorst, illustrated by Ray Cruz, text copyright © 1978 by Judith Viorst, illustrations copyright © 1978 by Ray Cruz.

Robert E. Barry: *The Musical Palm Tree* by Robert Barry, copyright © 1965 by Robert Barry, copyright renewed © 1993 by Robert Barry.

Curtis Brown, Ltd., and Lois L. Jones-Fax, Betty Ward, and Leon Speaks: "How Dog Outwitted Leopard" from *Tales from the Story Hat* by Verna Aardema, illustrated by Elton Fax, copyright © 1960 by Coward-McCann, illustrations copyright © 1960, 1995 by the Estate of Elton Fax.

Childrens Press, Inc., Chicago: *Picasso*, written and illustrated by Mike Venezia, copyright © 1988 by Childrens Press, Inc.

Dutton Children's Books, a division of Penguin Books USA Inc.: *The Cobbler's Song* by Marcia Sewall, copyright © 1982 by Marcia Sewall.

Farrar, Straus & Giroux, Inc.: *It Could Always Be Worse*, a Yiddish folk tale retold and illustrated by Margot Zemach, copyright © 1976 by Margot Zemach.

Aileen Fisher: "Houses" from *Up the Windy Hill* by Aileen Fisher, Abelard Press, New York, copyright 1953, copyright renewed 1981.

Greenwillow Books, a division of William Morrow and Co., Inc.: "Priscilla, Meet Felicity" from *Best Enemies* by Kathleen Leverich, text copyright © 1989 by Kathleen Leverich. "Tony and the Quarter" from *Rolling Harvey Down the Hill* by Jack Prelutsky, illustrated by Victoria Chess, text copyright © 1980 by Jack Prelutsky, illustrations copyright © 1980 by Victoria Chess.

Harcourt Brace & Co.: *Teammates* by Peter Golenbock, illustrated by Paul Bacon, text copyright © 1990 by Golenbock Communications, illustrations copyright © 1990 by Paul Bacon. "Fog" from *Chicago Poems* by Carl Sandburg, copyright 1916 by Holt Rinehart and Winston, Inc., renewed 1944 by Carl Sandburg.

HarperCollins Publishers: *Stevie* by John Steptoe, copyright © 1969 by John L. Steptoe. *Janey* by Charlotte Zolotow, text copyright © 1973 by Charlotte Zolotow. *Through Grandpa's Eyes* by Patricia MacLachlan, illustrated by Deborah Ray, text copyright © 1979 by Patricia MacLachlan, illustrations copyright © 1980 by Ray Studios, Inc. "Two Big Bears" from *Little House in the Big Woods* by Laura Ingalls Wilder, illustrated by Garth Williams, text copyright 1932 by Laura Ingalls Wilder, copyright © renewed 1960 by Roger L. MacBride, pictures copyright 1953 by Garth Williams, copyright © renewed 1981 by Garth Williams. "Smart" from *Where the Sidewalk Ends: The Poems and Drawings of Shel Silverstein*, copyright © 1974 by Shel Silverstein.

Holiday House: *Four Dollars and Fifty Cents* by Eric A. Kimmel, illustrated by Glen Rounds, text copyright © 1989 by Eric A. Kimmel, illustrations copyright © 1989 by Glen Rounds.

Houghton Mifflin Co. (School Department): "The Legend of Damon and Pythias" from *The Bag of Fire and Other Plays*, edited by Fan Kissen, copyright © 1964 by Houghton Mifflin Co., renewed © 1993 by John Kissen Heaslip.

Alfred A. Knopf, Inc.: "Gloria Who Might Be My Best Friend" from *The Stories Julian Tells* by Ann Cameron, illustrated by Ann Strugnell, text copyright © 1981 by Ann Cameron, illustrations copyright © 1981 by Ann Strugnell. *A New Coat for Anna* by Harriet Ziefert, illustrated by Anita Lobel, text copyright © 1986 by Harriet Ziefert, illustrations copyright © 1986 by Anita Lobel.

Lothrop, Lee & Shepard Books, a division of William Morrow and Co., Inc.: "The Apple" from *Eats* by Arnold Adoff, text copyright © 1979 by Arnold Adoff. *Roxaboxen* by Alice McLerran, illustrated by Barbara Cooney, text copyright © 1991 by Alice McLerran, illustrations copyright © 1991 by Barbara Cooney.

Margaret K. McElderry Books, an imprint of Macmillan Publishing Co.: "The Cat Who Became a Poet" from *Nonstop Nonsense* by Margaret Mahy, illustrated by Quentin Blake, text copyright © 1977 by Margaret Mahy, illustrations copyright © 1977 by Quentin Blake.

McGraw-Hill, Inc.: *The Blind Men and the Elephant* by J. G. Saxe.

National Geographic *World*: "Kids in Business," copyright © 1989 National Geographic Society.

5

*continued on page 287*

# FRIENDSHIP
❀

*7* ❧

# IMAGINATION

9 ❧

# MONEY

11 🌼

Sylvie Wickstrom

# GLORIA
# WHO MIGHT BE
# MY BEST FRIEND

Ann Cameron
*illustrated by Ann Strugnell*

If you have a girl for a friend, people find out and tease you. That's why I didn't want a girl for a friend—not until this summer, when I met Gloria.

It happened one afternoon when I was walking down the street by myself. My mother was visiting a friend of hers, and Huey was visiting a friend of his. Huey's friend is five and so I think he is too young to play with. And there aren't any kids just my age. I was walking down the street feeling lonely.

A block from our house I saw a moving van in front of a brown house, and men were carrying in chairs and tables and bookcases and boxes full of I don't know what. I watched for a while, and suddenly I heard a voice right behind me.

"Who are you?"

I turned around and there was a girl in a yellow dress. She looked the same age as me. She had curly hair that was braided into two pigtails with red ribbons at the ends.

"I'm Julian," I said. "Who are you?"

"I'm Gloria," she said. "I come from Newport. Do you know where Newport is?"

I wasn't sure, but I didn't tell Gloria. "It's a town on the ocean," I said.

"Right," Gloria said. "Can you turn a cartwheel?"

She turned sideways herself and did two cartwheels on the grass.

I had never tried a cartwheel before, but I tried to copy Gloria. My hands went down in the grass, my feet went up in the air, and— I fell over.

I looked at Gloria to see if she was laughing at me. If she was laughing at me, I was going to go home and forget about her.

But she just looked at me very seriously and said, "It takes practice," and then I liked her.

"I know where there's a bird's nest in your yard," I said.

"Really?" Gloria said. "There weren't any trees in the yard, or any birds, where I lived before."

I showed her where a robin lives and has eggs. Gloria stood up on a branch and looked in. The eggs were small and pale blue. The mother robin squawked at us, and she and the father robin flew around our heads.

"They want us to go away," Gloria said. She got down from the branch, and we went around to the front of the house and watched the moving men carry two rugs and a mirror inside.

"Would you like to come over to my house?" I said.

"All right," Gloria said, "if it is all right with my mother." She ran in the house and asked.

It was all right, so Gloria and I went to my house, and I showed her my room and my games and my rock collection, and then I made strawberry Kool-Aid and we sat at the kitchen table and drank it.

"You have a red mustache on your mouth," Gloria said.

"You have a red mustache on your mouth, too," I said.

Gloria giggled, and we licked off the mustaches with our tongues.

"I wish you'd live here a long time," I told Gloria.

Gloria said, "I wish I would too."

"I know the best way to make wishes," Gloria said.

"What's that?" I asked.

"First you make a kite. Do you know how to make one?"

"Yes," I said, "I know how." I know how to make good kites because my father taught me. We make them out of two crossed sticks and folded newspaper.

"All right," Gloria said, "that's the first part of making wishes that come true. So let's make a kite."

We went out into the garage and spread out sticks and newspaper and made a kite. I fastened on the kite string and went to the closet and got rags for the tail.

"Do you have some paper and two pencils?" Gloria asked. "Because now we make the wishes."

I didn't know what she was planning, but I went in the house and got pencils and paper.

"All right," Gloria said. "Every wish you want to have come true you write on a long thin piece of paper. You don't tell me your wishes, and I don't tell you mine. If you tell, your wishes don't come true. Also, if you look at the other person's wishes, your wishes don't come true."

Gloria sat down on the garage floor again and started writing her wishes. I wanted to see what they were—but I went to the other side of the garage and wrote my own wishes instead. I wrote:

1. I wish the fig tree would be the tallest in town.
2. I wish I'd be a great soccer player.
3. I wish I could ride in an airplane.
4. I wish Gloria would stay here and be my best friend.

I folded my four wishes in my fist and went over to Gloria.

"How many wishes did you make?" Gloria asked.

"Four," I said. "How many did you make?"

"Two," Gloria said.

I wondered what they were.

"Now we put the wishes on the tail of the kite," Gloria said. "Every time we tie one piece of rag on the tail, we fasten a wish in the knot. You can put yours in first."

I fastened mine in, and then Gloria fastened in hers, and we carried the kite into the yard.

"You hold the tail," I told Gloria, "and I'll pull."

We ran through the back yard with the kite, passed the garden and the fig tree, and went into the open field beyond our yard.

The kite started to rise. The tail jerked heavily like a long white snake. In a minute the kite passed the roof of my house and was climbing toward the sun.

We stood in the open field, looking up at it. I was wishing I would get my wishes.

"I know it's going to work!" Gloria said.

"How do you know?"

"When we take the kite down," Gloria told me, "there shouldn't be one wish in the tail. When the wind takes all your wishes, that's when you know it's going to work."

The kite stayed up for a long time. We both held the string. The kite looked like a tiny black spot in the sun, and my neck got stiff from looking at it.

"Shall we pull it in?" I asked.

"All right," Gloria said.

We drew the string in more and more until, like a tired bird, the kite fell at our feet.

We looked at the tail. All our wishes were gone. Probably they were still flying higher and higher in the wind.

Maybe I would get to be a good soccer player and have a ride in an airplane and the tallest fig tree in town. And Gloria would be my best friend.

"Gloria," I said, "did you wish we would be friends?"

"You're not supposed to ask me that!" Gloria said.

"I'm sorry," I answered. But inside I was smiling. I guessed one thing Gloria wished for. I was pretty sure we would be friends.

19

## MEET ANN CAMERON, AUTHOR

*Ann Cameron says that people often come to her with ideas for a story—as if writers were like piggy banks waiting for a coin to be dropped in. "But," she says, "stories are not like that. My story will never be exactly like yours. I could never tell yours for you. Your story, if it's really the way you want to tell it, can never be wrong the way an arithmetic answer is wrong; and even if your mother, your father, your teacher, or your best friend doesn't understand it, it's still right for you. Right answers in arithmetic are the same for everybody; but stories are individual, special, and all different—brand new thought-flowers blooming in the garden of your head."*

# BEAUTY AND THE BEAST

*illustrated by Pamela R. Levy*

Once upon a time there lived a very rich merchant who had three sons and three daughters. The girls were all beautiful, but the youngest was so lovely that she was called Beauty. This made her sisters very jealous.

Beauty was not only prettier than her sisters, but she was also smarter than they were. And unlike them, she was both helpful and kind. The sisters hated her for her kind heart and laughed at her because she spent her time reading good books instead of going to parties and balls as they did.

Suddenly, misfortune came to Beauty's father. He lost all of his money in business and every one of his ships at sea. All he had left was a small farm in the country. There he and his sons worked in the fields. Beauty got up each day at dawn. She lit the fires, cleaned the house, and prepared the meals. Though it was hard work, Beauty never complained. Her sisters, however, did nothing but complain. They did no work themselves, but just watching Beauty made them cross.

After a year, news came that one of their father's ships had not been lost but, filled to the top with riches, had sailed safely into port. Before their father left to meet the ship, the older sisters asked him to bring back some jewels and dresses for them. Beauty did not ask for anything.

"What shall I bring for you, Beauty?" her father asked.

"The only wish I have is to see you come home safely," she answered.

"But surely there is something you would like to have," said her father.

"Well, dear Father, then bring me a rose," said Beauty. "I love roses very much, and I have not seen one for a very long time."

In town, the merchant used most of the money from the ship's cargo to pay old debts. He started home as poor as when he had left. Deep snow and bitter frost made it impossible for his horse to carry him home that evening.

Night fell, and wolves were howling all around him. The merchant had lost his way in the deep forest, when suddenly he saw lights shining among the trees. When he hurried closer, he saw a magnificent castle standing in a beautiful park. He went through the open gate, got off his horse, and entered the castle. He saw nobody and heard not a sound.

The merchant sat down in front of a friendly fire, where a delicious dinner was waiting for him. He ate the dinner with much pleasure and hoped that he could soon thank his good host, but nobody appeared. He fell asleep after his meal and did not wake up until late the next morning. Next to him he saw a fine new suit in place of his old one.

"A kind fairy must own this castle," the merchant thought, but he did not see or hear any sign of life in the whole palace. Finally he went down into the lovely garden, where birds were singing and flowers were blooming. The beautiful roses reminded him of Beauty's wish, and he picked one of them.

Just then he heard a terrible roar, and a frightful Beast rushed up. It seemed to be very angry and said in a terrible voice, "Why are you stealing my roses? Did I not shelter you in my palace? Is this the way you say thank you? For this I shall kill you!"

The merchant was terrified. He threw himself on his knees and begged for mercy.

"I meant no harm, Your Majesty. I took the rose for one of my daughters. She asked me to bring her one. Please forgive me, Your Majesty."

"My name is not Majesty," roared the creature. "My name is Beast. I do not like to be flattered. Go home to your daughters. Ask whether one of them is willing to die for you. If they refuse, you must return yourself."

The merchant turned pale at the thought, but he promised to come back. He thought, I'll go and say farewell to my family. He found his horse already saddled, and soon he was home. He gave Beauty the rose and said, "Beauty, here is your rose. I had to pay a high price for it."

Then he told his daughters all that had happened. The older daughters wept loudly and begged their father not to go back. But Beauty said, "You have to keep your promise to the Beast, and I will go with you, dear Father."

But her father shook his head. "I will not let you go. I will go alone. I am old, and I shall die soon anyway."

Beauty stood firm. "Father, I *must* go," she said. "I would die of grief if I caused your death."

So Beauty said good-bye to her sisters and brothers and bravely mounted the horse with her father. Soon they reached the palace. In the dining hall they found a table set for two with golden plates, crystal glasses, and delicious food. They sat down to eat. Beauty thought, the Beast wants to fatten me up so that I will taste better when he eats me.

After dinner they heard the Beast's footsteps coming closer and closer. Beauty trembled and clung to her father. The Beast entered with a loud roar. Beauty was certain that he would eat her, but she tried to hide her fear and greeted him politely.

"Did you come willingly?" asked the Beast in his terrible voice.

"Yes," answered Beauty.

"You are very good. I am pleased with you," said the Beast. "Your father must leave tomorrow, and he can never come back. Good night, Beauty."

"Good night, Beast," she said.

Beauty went to bed, and as she slept that night, she saw

a beautiful fairy in her dreams. The fairy said, "Beauty, you have a good heart, and you shall be rewarded."

After her father had left the next morning, Beauty wept. She thought that the Beast would surely eat her this very night. Bravely she tried not to worry. "I'll enjoy my last day and explore the palace," she said to herself. She walked through many rooms. She found each one more brilliant than the last, until finally she came to a door marked *Beauty's Apartment*.

She opened the door timidly, and there she saw the room of her dreams. There were shelves of books, a piano, music, beautiful needlework for her to do, and everything else she could wish for. That night, as she sat down to supper, she heard the Beast coming. She began to tremble, for she wondered if he meant to eat her now.

The Beast only said gruffly, "Good evening, Beauty," and sat down and kept her company during the dinner.

"Everything here is yours," he said after a while. "Your wish is law. I hope that you will be happy here. I am only a stupid Beast. Tell me, do you find me very ugly?"

"Yes," said Beauty. "I cannot lie, but I think you are also very good and kind and not stupid at all."

Beauty had almost forgotten to be afraid of the monster when he asked her, "Do you love me, Beauty? Will you marry me?"

Beauty was silent. At last she said honestly, "No, Beast, I cannot marry you."

The Beast sighed deeply and then left the room.

Three months passed. Beauty had everything she could wish for. She had become used to the ugliness of the Beast. She even looked forward to the evenings, when he always came to talk to her. He was so good and kind that she liked him more and more.

Every night he asked her to marry him. One night Beauty said, "Beast, you are my best friend, and you are very dear to me, but I don't think I shall ever be able to marry you."

"Beauty," said the Beast, "I will die without you. Please promise that you will never leave me." Beauty became very sad. She was very homesick for her father and longed to see him once more. She begged the Beast to let her go.

"Please let me go home for a week, Beast. We are good friends, and I promise to come back."

"Very well. I cannot let you suffer," said the Beast. "But if you are not back in one week, your faithful Beast will die. When you are ready to come back, you have only to turn your ring on your finger." And the Beast sighed even more loudly than usual.

The next morning when Beauty woke up, she was in her father's house. She dressed in the gold and diamond gown that the kind Beast had sent, and she went to greet her father. How happy the merchant was when he saw his daughter! He hugged and kissed her and laughed and cried for joy all at the same time.

Beauty's brothers had joined the army, but her sisters, who were married now and who lived close by, came to see her. They were not at all happy to see Beauty dressed like a queen, looking lovelier than ever before. In their jealousy they planned to keep her longer than seven days so that she would break her promise to the Beast.

"Perhaps then he will eat her," they said. They treated Beauty so well and put on such a show of kindness that Beauty agreed to stay another week.

On the tenth night, Beauty dreamed that the Beast was lying on the grass in his garden, dying of despair. "Oh, my poor Beast," she cried. "He cannot help being ugly. He has a good and kind heart, and that is worth more than anything."

She turned her ring on her finger and at once found herself back in her beautiful palace. She looked everywhere for her Beast. Then she remembered her dream, and she ran into the garden. There lay the Beast, quite still.

"What if I have killed him?" thought Beauty, terrified.

Beauty forgot the Beast's ugliness and bent over him. His heart was still beating faintly. Suddenly he opened his eyes. He whispered to her, "I cannot live without you. Now that you are here, I will die happy."

"No, Beast, you cannot die," cried Beauty. "I never knew how much I loved you until now. I was afraid that I was too late to save your life. I cannot live without you, dear Beast. Let me be your wife."

As Beauty spoke these words, a blaze of light sprang up through the whole palace. Music filled the air. Suddenly the Beast disappeared, and in his place stood a handsome prince.

"Where is my Beast?" cried Beauty.

"I am he," answered the prince. "I was turned into a Beast by a powerful witch. Only a beautiful girl who would love me for my kind heart could break the spell. Only you could help me, for you love goodness more than beauty and riches. Please, Beauty, be my queen."

Beauty gave the prince her hand, and he led her into the castle. There Beauty found her father and all her family. The fairy who had appeared in Beauty's dream had brought them all there. What joy and happiness!

"Beauty," said the fairy, "you will be a great queen. You will find beauty, wisdom, and goodness in the prince, who loves you. This is the reward for your good heart."

Beauty and her prince were married in great splendor, and they lived happily ever after.

# ANGEL CHILD, DRAGON CHILD

Michele Maria Surat

*illustrated by Vo-Dinh Mai*

My sisters skipped through the stone gate two by two. Mother was not there to skip with me. Mother was far away in Vietnam. She could not say, "Ut, my little one, be an Angel Child. Be happy in your new American school."

I hugged the wall and peeked around the corner.

A boy with fire-colored hair pointed his finger. "Pajamas!" he shouted. "They wore white pajamas to school!" The American children tilted back their long noses, laughing.

I turned away. "I want to go home to Father and Little Quang," I said.

Chi Hai's hands curved over my shoulders. "Children stay where parents place them, Ut. We stay."

Somewhere, a loud bell jangled. I lost my sisters in a swirl of rushing children. "Pa-jaa-mas!" they teased.

Inside, the children did not sit together and chant as I was taught. Instead, they waved their hands and said their lessons one by one. I hid my hands, but the teacher called my name. "Nguyen Hoa."

Hoa is my true name, but I am Ut. Ut is my at-home name—a tender name for smallest daughter.

"Hoa," the teacher said slowly. "Write your name, please." She pressed a chalk-piece to my hand and wrote in the air.

31

"I not understand," I whispered. The round-eyed children twittered. The red-haired boy poked my back.

"Stand up, Pajamas!"

I stood and bowed. "*Chao buoi sang*," I said like an Angel Child. The children screeched like bluejays.

I sat down and flipped up my desk top, hiding my angry Dragon face.

Deep in my pocket, I felt Mother's gift—a small wooden matchbox with silvery edges. I took it out and traced the *hoa-phuong* on the lid. When I tapped the tiny drawer, Mother's eyes peeked over the edge.

"I will keep you safe in here, Mother," I told her. "See? You will just fit beside the crayons."

Her listening face smiled. In my heart, I heard the music of her voice. "Do not be angry, my smallest daughter," she said. "Be my brave little Dragon."

So all day I was brave, even when the children whispered behind their hands and the clock needles ticked slowly. Finally, the bell trilled. Time for home!

As soon as he saw me, Little Quang crowed, "Ut! Ut! Ut!" His laughing eyes gleamed like watermelon seeds. I dropped my books and slung him on my hip.

There he rode, tugging my hair as I sorted mint leaves and chives. Little Quang strung rice noodles from the cup hooks. Father and I laughed at this happy play.

At night, small brother curled tight beside me. I showed him Mother's lonely face inside the matchbox. Together we prayed, "Keep Mother safe. Send her to us soon." With Mother's picture near, we slept like Angel Children.

In this way, many days passed.

One day at school, small feathers floated past the frosty windows. "Mother," I whispered, "this is snow. It makes everything soft, even the angry trees with no leaves to make them pretty."

My fingers danced on the desk top while I waited for the bell. When it rang, I rushed out the door.

Outside, snowflakes left wet kisses on my cheeks. "Chi Hai!" I called. "Catch some!"

"It disappears!" she cried.

33 🌀

Just as Chi Hai spoke, a snowrock stung her chin. That red-haired boy darted behind the dumpster. He was laughing hard.

I tried, but I could not be a noble Dragon. Before I knew it, I was scooping up snow. My hands burned and my fingers turned red. I threw my snowrock and the laughing stopped.

Suddenly, the boy tackled me! We rolled in the snow, kicking and yelling, until the principal's large hand pinched my shoulder.

"Inside!" he thundered, and he marched us to our classroom.

"We can't have this fighting. You two have to help each other," ordered the principal. He pointed at me. "Hoa, you need to speak to Raymond. Use our words.

Tell him about Vietnam." Raymond glared. "And you, Raymond, you must learn to listen. You will write Hoa's story."

"But I can't understand her funny words," Raymond whined. "Anyway, I don't have a pencil."

"Use this one, then," said the principal. He slapped down a pencil, turned and slammed the door. His shoes squeegeed down the hall.

"Pajamas!" Raymond hissed. He crinkled his paper and snapped the pencil in two. He hid his head in his arms. How could I tell my story to *him*?

The clock needles blurred before my eyes. No! I *would not* be an Angel Child for this cruel-hearted boy.

But later, across the room, I heard a sniffle. Raymond's shoulders jiggled like Little Quang's when he cried for Mother.

I crept over. Gently, I tugged the sad boy's sleeve. He didn't move. "Raymond," I pleaded, "not cry. I give you cookie."

Suddenly, his head bounced up. "Hoa!" he shouted. "You said my name. You didn't use funny words." He broke off a piece of the cookie.

"I say English," I answered proudly. "And you call me Ut. Ut is my at-home name, from Vietnam."

"Okay, *Ut*," he mumbled. "But only if you tell me what's in your matchbox."

"My mother," I told him. We giggled and ate the cookie crumbs.

Then Raymond asked, "Why do you need your mother's picture?"

"Mother is far away," I said softly.

"She didn't come with you?"

"So many children in my family," I sighed. "No money for Mother to come."

"Wait," said Raymond. He grabbed part of the broken pencil. I handed him a new sheet of paper. "Now tell me about Vietnam," he said.

Raymond scrawled my words in black squiggles. I crayoned pictures in the margins.

When we were ready, Raymond leaned out the door. "Done!" he beamed. He waved the story like a flag.

The principal squeegeed up the hall. "You may go," said the big man.

We dashed through the stone gate together.

The next day, the principal read our story to the whole school. "These girls sailed many oceans to be here. They left behind their home, their friends, and most important of all, their mother. So now . . ."

"Ut's mother needs money for the long boat ride to America!" shouted a familiar voice. Raymond stood on his chair. "And we could have a fair and *earn* the money."

"Young man!" warned the principal.

Raymond slid down in his seat. "We could," he insisted. I hid my eyes. I held my breath. Chi Hai squeezed my hand.

"A special fair! A Vietnamese fair!" my teacher exclaimed. My eyes opened wide.

The principal's eyebrows wiggled like caterpillars. "But who will help with a Vietnamese fair?"

37

"Me!" cried Raymond.

"We will!" squealed the children.

"Well, what are we waiting for?" said the principal. And we all clapped for the fair.

On the special day, I wore my white *ao dai* and welcomed everyone to our Vietnamese fair. "*Chao buoi sang,*" I said, bowing like an Angel Child.

"*Chao buoi sang,*" they answered, smiling.

High above our heads, our rainbow dragon floated freely. Below, Chi Hai and her friends sold rice cakes, imperial rolls and sesame cookies. Raymond popped balloons and won three goldfish. He gave one to Little Quang. "Don't eat it," he warned.

By the end of the day, we had just enough money to send to Mother. "When will she come?" I wondered.

Every day, we walked home wondering, "When will Mother come?"

We slid through icy winter. . . .

We splish-splashed through spring rain. . . .

We tiptoed barefoot through the grass, still hoping she would come.

On the last day of school, when I knew the *hoa-phuong* were blossoming in Vietnam, Raymond and I raced home faster than all my sisters. We were the first to see Father and Little Quang at the picture window, and beside them . . .

Mother!

39

### MEET MICHELE MARIA SURAT, AUTHOR

*When she is not writing, Michele Maria Surat teaches high school near Washington, D.C. The tale of Ut, the character in this story, began when a Vietnamese student came to Surat with tear-filled eyes and shared a photograph of her mother in Vietnam. Surat wanted to tell the story of these brave children in hopes of creating an understanding between Vietnamese and American children. She wished to show the sensitive spirits of these determined newcomers to America.*

### MEET VO-DINH MAI, ILLUSTRATOR

*Vo-Dinh Mai was born in Vietnam. As a boy there, he enjoyed visiting and observing a local woodcut artist. He has published books as a writer, translator, and illustrator. He is married to Helen Coutant, also a well-known children's author.*

# STEVIE
## John Steptoe

O ne day my momma told me, "You know you're gonna have a little friend come stay with you."

And I said, "Who is it?"

And she said, "You know my friend Mrs. Mack? Well she has to work all week and I'm gonna keep her little boy."

I asked, "For how long?"

She said, "He'll stay all week and his mother will come pick him up on Saturdays."

The next day the doorbell rang. It was a lady and a kid. He was smaller than me. I ran to my mother. "Is that them?"

They went in the kitchen but I stayed out in the hall to listen.

The little boy's name was Steven but his mother kept calling him Stevie. My name is Robert but my momma don't call me Robertie.

And so Steve moved in, with his old crybaby self. He always had to have his way. And he was greedy too. Everything he sees he wants. "Could I have somma that? Gimme this." Man!

Since he was littler than me, while I went to school he used to stay home and play with my toys.

I wished his mother would bring somma *his* toys over here to break up.

I used to get so mad at my mother when I came home after school. "Momma, can't you watch him and tell him to leave my stuff alone?"

Then he used to like to get up on my bed to look out the window and leave his dirty footprints all over my bed. And my momma never said nothin' to him.

And on Saturdays when his mother comes to pick him up, he always tries to act cute just cause his mother is there.

He picked up my airplane and I told him not to bother it. He thought I wouldn't say nothin' to him in front of his mother.

I could never go anywhere without my mother sayin' "Take Stevie with you now."

"But why I gotta take him everywhere I go?" I'd say.

"Now if you were stayin' with someone you wouldn't want them to treat you mean," my mother told me. "Why don't you and Stevie try to play nice?"

Yeah, but I always been nice to him with his old spoiled self. He's always gotta have his way anyway. I had to take him out to play with me and my friends.

"Is that your brother, Bobby?" they'd ask me.

"No."

"Is that your cousin?"

"No! He's just my friend and he's stayin' at my house and my mother made me bring him."

"Ha, ha. You gotta baby-sit! Bobby the baby-sitter!"

"Aw, be quiet. Come on, Steve. See! Why you gotta make all my friends laugh for?"

"Ha, ha. Bobby the baby-sitter," my friends said.

"Hey, come on, y'all, let's go play in the park. You comin', Bobby?" one of my friends said.

"Naw, my momma said he can't go in the park cause the last time he went he fell and hurt his knee, with his old stupid self."

43

And then they left.

"You see? You see! I can't even play with my friends. Man! Come on."

"I'm sorry, Robert. You don't like me, Robert? I'm sorry," Stevie said.

"Aw, be quiet. That's okay," I told him.

One time when my daddy was havin' company I was just sittin' behind the couch just listenin' to them talk and make jokes. And I wasn't makin' no noise. They didn't even know I was there!

Then here comes Stevie with his old loud self. Then when my father heard him, he yelled at *me* and told me to go upstairs.

Just cause of Stevie.

Sometimes people get on your nerves and they don't mean it or nothin' but they just bother you. Why I gotta put up with him? My momma only had one kid. I used to have a lot of fun before old stupid came to live with us.

One Saturday Steve's mother and father came to my house to pick him up like always. But they said that they were gonna move away and that Stevie wasn't gonna come back anymore.

So then he left. The next mornin' I got up to watch cartoons and I fixed two bowls of corn flakes. Then I just remembered that Stevie wasn't here.

Sometimes we had a lot of fun runnin' in and out of the house. Well, I guess my bed will stay clean from now on. But that wasn't so bad. He couldn't help it cause he was stupid.

I remember the time I ate the last piece of cake in the breadbox and blamed it on him.

We used to play Cowboys and Indians on the stoop.

I remember when I was doin' my homework I used to try to teach him what I had learned. He could write his name pretty good for his age.

I remember the time we played boogie man and we hid under the covers with Daddy's flashlight.

And that time we was playin' in the park under the bushes and we found these two dead rats and one was brown and one was black.

And him and me and my friends used to cook mickies or marshmallows in the park.

We used to have some good times together.

I think he liked my momma better than his own, cause he used to call his mother "Mother" and he called my momma "Mommy."

Aw, no! I let my corn flakes get soggy thinkin' about him.

He was a nice little guy.

He was kinda like a little brother.

Little Stevie.

45

MEET JOHN STEPTOE, AUTHOR
AND ILLUSTRATOR

*John Steptoe was a high-school student when he wrote and illustrated Stevie. He was mostly interested in studying art. As his first children's book, Stevie brought him national fame and many awards. About the book, Steptoe has said: "I wanted it to be something black children could read without translating the language, something real which would relate to what a black child would know." He went on to write and illustrate many more children's books.*

# JANEY
## Charlotte Zolotow
*illustrated by Leah
Palmer Preiss*

Janey
it's lonely
all day long
since you moved away.

When I walk in the rain
and the leaves are wet
and clinging to the sidewalk
I remember
how we used to walk
home from school
together.

I remember how you had to touch
everything we passed,
the wet leaves
of the privet hedge,
even the stucco part
of the wall.
I only look with my eyes.

I still have the pebble
you found on the playground.
And I remember how
you skipped flat rocks
into the pond.
Mine just sank.

Sometimes when I'm playing
with the other kids
I remember how your voice sounded.
No one else sounds like you.

I remember sometimes
we both talked at once
and when we stopped
we'd said the same thing.
And I remember sitting on the steps
in the sun and not talking
at all.

46

There is no one else
I can sit with
and not talk.

I remember how
we'd go home for dinner
and I could hardly wait
for dinner to end
to call you.
But sometimes you called me first.

And I remember last Christmas
I half didn't want
to give you your present,
I wanted it so much myself.

You told me later
you half didn't want to give me mine
but when we each opened our present
it was the *same* book.
I think of you every time
I read the stories over again.

When the wind blows
through the trees at night
I remember how we used to
listen together
nights you slept over.

I didn't want you to move away.
You didn't want to either.
Janey
maybe some day
we'll grow up
and live near each other
again.

I wish you hadn't moved away.

47

# PRISCILLA, MEET FELICITY

from BEST ENEMIES by Kathleen Leverich
*illustrated by Paul Meisel*

That September morning Priscilla woke up early. "Hurry and dress," said her mother. "You do not want to be late for the first day of school."

Priscilla washed her face. She brushed her teeth. She put on her favorite dress. She put on her socks and her shoes. She opened her drawer, took out her brand-new pencil case, and zipped it open. Inside lay a pink eraser, a blue ballpoint pen, a red marker, and two yellow pencils with sharp points. Priscilla zipped the case shut and carried it downstairs to breakfast.

"Rrrruf," barked her dog Pow-wow.

"Don't you look nice," said her mother.

"A regular little schoolgirl," said her father.

"Big deal," said her older sister Eve. "Would somebody please pass the orange juice?"

Priscilla felt a little nervous. "What if none of my friends are in my class?"

"Wrrouu," yipped Pow-wow.

Her mother placed a bowl of cereal in front of Priscilla. She gave her a hug. "Then you will meet new friends."

Priscilla was not so sure.

Priscilla and her mother read the class lists that were posted in the school's front hall.

"There is my name!" Priscilla pointed to the fourth list. "Priscilla Robin."

"Ms. Cobble's class," read Priscilla's mother. "Room 7."

"Is Jill in my class?" asked Priscilla.

"No," said her mother.

"Is Sue in my class?" said Priscilla. "Is Dennis?"

"I am afraid not." Priscilla's mother was looking down the list, too. "Here is a nice name, 'Felicity Doll.' She sounds like a brand-new friend."

Ms. Cobble stood in the doorway to Room 7. "Good morning." She shook hands with Priscilla's mother. "Good morning." She shook hands with Priscilla. "What a lovely new pencil case!"

Ms. Cobble gave Priscilla a big name tag to hang around her neck. "Go right inside," she told Priscilla. "Choose an empty desk and sit down."

Priscilla kissed her mother goodbye. She stepped into the classroom. Lots of boys and girls chattered in the room. Priscilla felt too shy to look at them carefully. She held her pencil case tightly. She looked at the desks.

Most of the desks had a flat top and an opening at one end where you could slide books inside. A few desks looked different. They were big and old. They were made of wood and had slanted tops. The tops opened upward like the top of Priscilla's toy chest. Priscilla watched a boy put his books inside one of those desks. He lifted the desktop high.

"Wow!" thought Priscilla. "I would like one of those desks with the slanty tops." She looked around the classroom. She saw an empty desk near the blackboard. It had a flat top. She saw an empty desk near the coat closet. It had a flat top. She saw an empty desk near the front of the room. It was big and old. It was made of wood and it had a slanty top. Priscilla hurried to the desk. She pulled out a chair and sat down.

"Hey!" said a voice.

Priscilla turned. Beside her stood a curly-haired girl. She wore a ruffly dress. The name on her name tag was too difficult for Priscilla to read.

"You will have to move," said the curly-haired girl. "This desk belongs to me."

Priscilla felt uncertain. Then she felt mad. "This desk was empty when I sat down," she told the curly-haired girl. Priscilla opened the desk. She put her pencil case inside. Beside it she put her lunch box. "This desk is mine."

The curly-haired girl looked at the pencil case. She looked at the lunch box. She smiled a snakey smile at Priscilla. "We could share this desk. Sharing would be the fair thing to do."

"I don't want to share," said Priscilla.

The curly-haired girl poked her in the chest. "Let me share this desk, or I will tell Ms. Cobble you are being selfish."

Priscilla pushed the curly-haired girl's finger away. "All right. But just for now."

"Oh, boy!" said the girl. She dragged up a chair. She jammed it next to Priscilla's. "Move over!" Priscilla had to sit so that one leg was under the desk and one leg was outside it.

At the front of the room Ms. Cobble clapped her hands. "Let's settle down, class."

"Hey," the curly-haired girl nudged Priscilla. She pointed to Priscilla's name tag. "What does that say?"

"Priscilla," she said. She looked at the curly-haired girl's name tag. "What does yours say?"

The curly-haired girl fluffed her curls. "Don't you know how to read?" She pointed to her tag and spelled, "F-e-l-i-c-i-t-y. Felicity Doll."

Ms. Cobble handed out paper. She handed out crayons. She said, "Now, class—"

Felicity raised her hand. "Ms. Cobble!" She waved her hand as hard as she could. "Ms. Cobble!"

"Is something wrong, Felicity?" said Ms. Cobble.

Felicity squirmed in her seat. "I cannot work very well. Priscilla is crowding me."

Ms. Cobble walked over to where they sat. "What are you two girls doing at the same desk? There are plenty of empty ones. Come, Priscilla. We'll find you a desk of your own."

"But—" said Priscilla.

"Come along," said Ms. Cobble. "We have more things to do this morning than choose desks." She led Priscilla to an ordinary desk with a flat top in the very back row of the classroom. "Now," she said. "Aren't you more comfortable at a desk of your own?"

"Ms. Cobble!" Felicity waved her hand. "Priscilla left this stuff in my desk." She took out Priscilla's lunch box and pencil case and carried them back to Priscilla's new desk.

"Thank you, Felicity," said Ms. Cobble. "I can see that you are going to be an outstanding Class Helper."

Ms. Cobble returned to the front of the room. Felicity returned to her seat.

"Now, class," said Ms. Cobble.

Felicity turned around. "Hey, Priscilla!" she whispered.

"What?"

Felicity stuck out her tongue. She covered her mouth and laughed a silent laugh.

"How was your first day of school?" said Priscilla's father that night at dinner.

"Terrible," said Priscilla.

"Rrrrgrrrr." Pow-wow lay under the table at her feet.

"Did you make new friends?" asked her mother.

"I made a new enemy," said Priscilla. "Her name is Felicity Doll. She stole my desk."

"Felicity Doll?" said Eve. "I know Felicity Doll. Felicity Doll is a real snake."

"Eve!" said Priscilla's mother. She was serving the salad.

"I am sure Felicity is a lovely girl, once you get to know her."

Eve shook her head. "The one thing worse than having Felicity Doll for an enemy would be having Felicity Doll for a friend."

"I do not need to worry about that," Priscilla said.

The next morning when Priscilla arrived at school she found Felicity waiting beside her desk.

"This is an okay desk," said Felicity. "But my desk is much nicer."

"You stole that desk from me," said Priscilla. She sat down in her chair. She took her pencil case out of her desk. She took out a piece of paper and began to copy the new words Ms. Cobble had written on the blackboard.

Felicity stood beside Priscilla's desk. "Don't be mad, Priscilla. It is not my fault that Ms. Cobble made you move." Felicity leaned on the desk. "I like you, Priscilla."

Priscilla looked up from her paper. She could not believe her ears.

Felicity grabbed Priscilla's hand and squeezed it. "Be my friend. You can sleep over at my house. You can sit next to me at my birthday party. . . ." Felicity smiled her snakey smile.

"I have never slept over at a friend's house," said Priscilla. "My sister Eve goes on sleep-overs all the time."

"I have canopy beds," coaxed Felicity. "I have a color TV in my room. . . ."

Priscilla freed her hand from Felicity's. "Canopy beds?" Perhaps Felicity was not so bad. "Very well," she said. "I will be your friend."

"Oh, boy!" said Felicity. "Now we can swap pencil cases." She grabbed Priscilla's brand-new pencil case. She pulled her own case from her pocket and dropped it on the desk.

Felicity's case was a mess. The zipper was broken. Inside were two stubby pencils with chew marks. Nothing else.

"I do not want to swap," said Priscilla.

"Just for today." Felicity smiled her snakey smile. "Friends share."

*Brnnnnggg!* The bell rang.

"So long, pal," Felicity took Priscilla's pencil case and hurried to her desk.

"Felicity!" Priscilla started after her.

"Priscilla, school has begun!" clapped Ms. Cobble. "No more visiting with Felicity. Sit down."

Priscilla sat.

"Now, class," said Ms. Cobble.

Felicity turned around at her desk. "Hey, Priscilla," she hissed. She waved Priscilla's pencil case and snickered.

"How was your second day of school?" asked Priscilla's father that night at dinner.

"Terrible!" said Priscilla.

"Rrrrgrr," barked Pow-wow from under the dinner table.

"Did you make new friends?" asked Priscilla's mother.

Priscilla stuck her fork prongs into the tablecloth. "Felicity Doll wants to be my friend."

"That's nice," said Priscilla's mother. She passed Priscilla a plate of beef stew. "I am glad you two girls made up."

"Pris-cil-la," said Eve. "May I see you for a moment in the kitchen?"

Priscilla followed Eve through the swinging door.

Pow-wow followed Priscilla.

Eve shook her head. "You've been at school two days, Priscilla, and you've already made a giant mistake."

"Making friends with Felicity?" guessed Priscilla.

"Felicity does not know how to be a friend," said Eve. "Felicity knows how to be a snake."

"Rrrrgrr," barked Pow-wow.

Priscilla nodded. "Yesterday Felicity stole my desk. Today she took my pencil case."

"You need someone to stick up for you," said Eve. "Do you want me to make Felicity give your things back?"

Priscilla wanted her things back. "But," she thought, "Felicity will trap me again with another one of her tricks. . . ."

"Eve?" called their mother from the dining room. "Priscilla? Dinner is getting cold!"

"Thank you," Priscilla told Eve. "But I think I'd better stick up for myself."

The next morning Felicity wanted to trade lunch boxes.

"I have a lunch box," said Priscilla. "You carry your lunch in a paper bag."

"Friends share." Felicity smiled her snakey smile.

Before Priscilla knew what happened, Felicity carried off Priscilla's lunch box. Felicity put the lunch box inside the

beautiful desk that should have been Priscilla's. She put it right next to the brand-new pencil case that Priscilla could only see from a distance.

At lunch Felicity spilled tomato juice on her pink sweater.

"Friends share," Felicity told Priscilla. Before Priscilla knew it, Felicity had taken Priscilla's soft yellow sweater.

"What will I do with this?" Priscilla wrinkled her nose. Felicity had left her the soggy pink mess.

"Felicity Doll has gone too far!" Eve said to Priscilla after dinner that night. "She took your pencil case, and your lunch box, and now your sweater—"

"Don't forget my desk," said Priscilla.

"She cannot push around my little sister!" Eve made a fist. "Tomorrow—"

"Eve," said Priscilla, "let me try one last time."

The next morning Priscilla arrived at school. Felicity waited beside her desk.

"I did not do my homework," said Felicity. "Lend me your paper. I will copy the answers."

Priscilla opened her mouth to say "NO!"

"Well?" said Felicity.

Priscilla shut her mouth. She had an idea. "Here is my homework." She handed Felicity her paper. She smiled a Felicity smile.

"Friends share," she said.

Felicity looked at the paper. She looked hard at Priscilla.

"Is there something wrong with this homework—?"

*Brnnnnggg!* The bell rang.

"Settle down, class." Ms. Cobble clapped her hands.

Felicity snatched Priscilla's paper and hurried to her seat.

Priscilla watched Felicity take off *her* soft yellow sweater. She watched Felicity hang it over the back of *her* chair. She watched Felicity take a brand-new pencil out of *her* pencil case. Felicity began to copy *her* homework—

"Ms. Cobble!" Priscilla raised her hand. She waved it.

Ms. Cobble turned from the blackboard. "Priscilla, whatever is the trouble?"

Priscilla took a deep breath. "Felicity Doll is sitting at my desk."

Ms. Cobble looked at Felicity. She looked at Priscilla. "We already settled this matter, Priscilla."

"Ask Felicity whose lunch box is in that desk," said Priscilla.

"Felicity?" said Ms. Cobble.

"Wel-l-l-l," said Felicity.

"Ask her whose pencil case is in that desk," said Priscilla.

Ms. Cobble looked stern.

"Uhnnn—" said Felicity.

"That is my yellow sweater hanging over the back of Felicity's chair," said Priscilla.

Ms. Cobble frowned.

Felicity looked at her feet.

"That is my homework on top of the desk," said Priscilla.

"Fe-li-city!" said Ms. Cobble. "Is this true?"

Felicity's voice sounded squeaky. "Yes."

"Priscilla," said Ms. Cobble. "Felicity, I think you had better change desks."

"I'll get you," hissed Felicity as she passed Priscilla.

Priscilla sat down at the beautiful desk. "I doubt it," she thought.

"How was school today?" asked Priscilla's father that night at dinner.

"Rrrruf," yipped Pow-wow.

"Excellent," said Priscilla.

Priscilla's mother asked, "Did you play with your friend, Felicity Doll?"

"Felicity Doll is no longer my friend," said Priscilla. "Please pass the brussels sprouts."

"Not your friend?" Priscilla's mother looked concerned. "Whatever happened?"

Eve choked on her macaroni. "Yes, Priscilla, tell us what happened."

Pow-wow yawned. "Eeeehh."

Priscilla took a sip of milk. She smoothed the sleeves of her soft yellow sweater. "After school today, Felicity stopped me. She told me that we are no longer friends. 'We are enemies!' she said."

Priscilla's mother sighed.

Priscilla's father shook his head.

"Felicity has a new best friend," said Priscilla. "Her name is Lucille Bingay."

"How sad!" said Eve, but she was giggling. "You must feel just awful."

Priscilla speared a brussels sprout. "I don't feel nearly as awful as poor Lucille."

61

# THE TREE HOUSE

Lois Lowry

*illustrated by Trina Schart Hyman*

It was a terrific tree house. *Better* than terrific: It was a marvelous, magnificent, one-of-a-kind tree house, with wooden walls painted bright blue. It had two windows, with red shutters on each, and a yellow door with two shiny brass hinges and a small brass bell that rang when you pulled a string. There was a little porch where you could sit with your legs dangling.

Inside were a table, a chair, a small rug with fringe on each end, and two fat pillows so that you could lie on the rug and read.

You reached it by climbing a ladder—a ladder to the best tree house ever. And it belonged to Chrissy.

"It's all mine, isn't it?" she had asked her grandfather after he built the house for her. "Just mine, and nobody else's?"

Grandpa was washing his paintbrush. He nodded. "I built it just for you," he said.

So Chrissy used her markers and made a sign. CHRISSY'S HOUSE, the sign said. KEEP OUT! She tacked it to the door. Then she took her favorite books into the tree house, curled up on the pillows, and began to read.

"Chrissy?" The voice came from the next yard, from just across the fence.

Chrissy got up and looked through the tree house window. "Hi, Leah," she said to the girl who lived next door. "How do you like my tree house, now that it's all done?"

"It's beautiful," Leah said. "What do you have inside?"

"A table and two chairs and a rug and some pillows," Chrissy told her. "And some secret stuff," she added, though she didn't have secret stuff, really. She *planned* to.

"Can I come up and see?" Leah asked.

"No," Chrissy said. "It's just for me. That's why I made the sign."

Leah stood silently for a moment. Then she said, "I hate you, Chrissy."

"I hate you, too," Chrissy replied. She went back to the pillows and opened her book again.

A short time later, she heard voices in the next yard. She peered through her window and saw that Leah's father was there with Leah. They had a wheelbarrow full of old boards, and a jar of nails. As Chrissy watched from her window, she saw Leah's father prop an old ladder against the trunk of the tree on the other side of the fence. Then, after he jiggled the ladder and made certain it was steady, he climbed up, carrying a board, and began to nail it into place where the branches came together.

He was making Leah a tree house. Chrissy laughed to herself. Leah's father was at home because he had lost his job. She knew they didn't have extra money now for things like paint and brass hinges. And Leah's tree house would never be as good as hers. Never in a million years. Chrissy went back to her book and turned the pages while the hammering continued.

That evening, after supper, Chrissy stood beside the fence and looked up at Leah's finished house. She laughed aloud.

It had taken a week for Grandpa to finish building her beautiful tree house. Grandpa had used new wooden boards from the lumberyard. But Leah's had been completed in a day, and Chrissy could see that it was made from the stack of old weathered boards that had been in the corner of Leah's yard. Only one board remained there now; the others had become the tree house.

The house had walls and a porch and a door and two windows, but it had no shutters and no paint and no door bell. The boards were crooked, and the roof had holes where the pieces of wood didn't quite meet.

Even the sign wasn't as good, because Leah had done hers with crayons instead of marking pens. But its message was the same. LEAH'S HOUSE, it said. KEEP OUT.

Leah's head appeared in the window of her tree house.

"Your house is not as nice as mine," Chrissy told her.

"Not on the outside," Leah said. "But inside, it's better."

Chrissy wondered what Leah had inside her tree house. But she didn't ask.

For several days the two girls didn't speak to each other. They sat alone in their tree houses. By the fourth day, Chrissy had finished all her books and had read some of them twice. She went to her window and called across the fence to Leah.

"Do you have any books I can borrow?" she asked, when Leah's head appeared.

"No. Our car's broken so we can't go to the library."

"You don't have any books at *all*?"

Leah shook her head.

Chrissy sat back down. She wondered what it would be like to be in a tree house with no books at all. She wondered what Leah was doing in there.

Finally she called across the fence again. "Would you like to borrow some of mine?" she asked. And Leah said yes.

So Chrissy climbed down, stood at the fence, and handed two books over to Leah, who had climbed down her ladder, too.

"I have some bananas," Leah told her. "Do you want one?" Chrissy nodded, and Leah climbed up and returned with a banana to pass across the fence.

Back in her own tree house, Chrissy peeled and ate the banana. Then she called to Leah again.

"Do you have a wastebasket in your house? I don't want to mess up my carpeting with this banana peel."

Leah, looking through her window, nodded. So Chrissy climbed down, and Leah climbed down, and Chrissy handed the banana peel across the fence.

Both girls climbed back into their houses. Chrissy sat alone and admired her fringed rug for a moment, then leafed through her books again, wondering what Leah was doing. She called through her window.

"Leah?"

Leah looked out. "What?"

"I could come visit you if you want," Chrissy said.

Leah didn't answer.

"Or you could come visit me," Chrissy added.

"Your sign says KEEP OUT," Leah pointed out. "So does mine."

"Well," Chrissy suggested, "we could change them."

"That's it." Clancy hung it on the back of a chair and rubbed his hands together. "Powerful cold out." He eyed the brown teapot with the steam rising from its spout.

Tippitt made no move to take another mug from the dresser. "You said you wouldn't be staying."

"Right," Clancy said. "When will the coat be ready?"

"By Saturday."

"I'll be here for it."

Tippitt and Sam watched Clancy go. "It was a sorry day when Bridget got in his vegetables," Tippitt said. "He's a great man for his growing things. It comes from having neither chick nor child to call his own."

Sam nodded, the way he always did when Tippitt talked to him.

"Though my own children's grown and my wife is gone I still have you, my good cow, and my wee hen. All he has are his cabbages and turnips. It's not much when all's said and done."

Sam nodded again and Tippitt examined the coat. "It'll be as easy to do as skimming cream," he said. "And it'll be done for Saturday."

It would have been, too, except that the night was extra cold, and in the middle of it Tippitt heard Bridget mooing in the barn. When he got up and looked for something to put round her to keep her warm, there was Clancy's coat. Tippitt took it out, spread it over the cow, and forgot all about it till the next Saturday when he was having dinner and looked out to see Clancy heading up the road.

"Jakers!" Tippitt said to Sam. "Didn't I forget all about Clancy's coat! We'd better invite him to stay a while this time, for he'll be powerful annoyed and in need of soothing."

"Come in, come in," he called from the open door as Sam nodded and wagged his tail.

Clancy took off his muffler and set it on the dresser.

"I see you're eating your dinner," he said. "I'll not keep you, for I only came for my old coat."

"It's not ready yet," Tippitt said. "It's been over my . . . over . . . overlooked. But . . ."

"Moo . . . oooo!" Bridget called from the barn.

"I'll have it for you for certain sure by next Saturday," Tippitt said quickly. "Would you have a cup of tea before you go?" He poured it from the pot, thick as tar and black as night.

"You always did make a good cup of tea." Clancy sat down at the table and eyed the remains of Tippitt's dinner. "Watery looking potatoes you have there. I'm thinking you bought those from O'Donnell of the Glen?"

"Aye," Tippitt said. "And they're like candle grease."

Clancy finished his tea and stood up. "I'll be back for the coat on Saturday."

When he opened the door the March wind came in. "I'll be glad of that old coat," Clancy said, winding his muffler tight round his neck. "There's a lot of use in it yet."

Sam and Tippitt watched till he got all the way to his own wee house down the road, and then Tippitt went to the barn and got the coat from where Bridget was lying on it. And a hard job she made of it, for she didn't want to give it up.

Tippitt shook the hairs from it and set it next to his sewing machine. "I'll start on you in the morning," he told it. And he would have.

Only, that night the wind came up with a terrible fierceness and it blew the whole back window out of Tippitt's house, waking him from a sound sleep. In his hurry to find something to keep out the cold Tippitt saw the coat. He tacked it up where the glass had been and forgot all about it.

The next Saturday Clancy knocked at the door.

"Jakers save us!" Tippitt told Sam. "And the coat's not ready yet! This will take some quick thinking."

He pulled the best chair close to the fire and plumped out the cushions, and he and Sam were both smiling as they met Clancy at the door.

"Come in, sit down," Tippitt invited. "The coat's not fixed yet. It's been in my . . . in my . . . in my mind since I saw you last. But it'll be done by next Saturday for certain sure."

Tippitt noticed that Clancy had a sack slung over his shoulder. "What's this?" he asked.

"Potatoes," Clancy said. "I have them going to waste and I can't stand to see anybody eating poison like the ones you were eating last week. Not even you, Tippitt."

"Well, I'm much obliged." Tippitt decided to ignore the last part of the speech. "Will you have a cup of tea and a piece of my fresh baked bread before you go?"

He sliced a piece, spread it with butter, and carried it to where Clancy had seated himself in the best chair with its plumped up cushions.

"You always did have the whitest bread and the sweetest butter," Clancy said. "I can't buy the likes of it anywhere."

"It's Bridget's good buttermilk that goes into the both of them," Tippitt told him, and wished he'd been quiet because mention of Bridget might remind Clancy and set him off on another uproar.

But Clancy only said: "It's the care you give her. It shows up in what she gives back. Same as me and my garden."

Jakers, Tippitt thought, here it comes. But no more came.

"Saturday, then," Clancy said as he was leaving and Tippitt and Sam both nodded.

As soon as he'd gone Tippitt got the coat from the back window and nailed a piece of wood in its place. He put the coat on top of his sewing machine. "Don't be going any place else," he scolded it. "I'm getting to you tomorrow."

And he would have. Except that the very next day he remembered that he'd promised Rosie O'Brien her skirt for the Friday dance, so he threw Clancy's coat into the corner till he had time to get at it, and Mary, his hen, came right in and set herself on it. And the first thing Tippitt heard was her clucking and panting and swishing her feathers to get herself comfortable before laying her eggs.

Tippitt scratched his head. "Jakers, Sam! It wouldn't be decent to move Mary, and her in the middle of her business. We'll just have to put Clancy off again and we'll have to be smart about it."

On Saturday Tippitt moved his old sofa so that it hid Mary and the coat. He wrapped a big square of yellow butter and set it and a fresh brown loaf in the middle of the table.

"Och, the coat's not finished yet, Clance," he said when Clancy arrived and before he could ask.

"But there's good work being done on it, I'll promise you that."

Then he pointed to the butter and the bread. "I've a couple of wee presents for you here."

"It's a long time since you called me 'Clance'," Clancy said gruffly. He set another sack on the table. "Here's a cabbage for you, and a bundle of leeks and carrots." His eyes slid away from Tippitt's and Tippitt knew he was wishing he'd never said 'garden' the week before just as Tippitt had wished he'd never said 'cow'.

They had tea together, sitting one on each side of the table, the fire flickering and the wee room as warm as toast. Tippitt asked about Clancy's bad leg and Clancy inquired about Tippitt's niece, the one who was married to a policeman and living in America.

"It's almost like old times," Clancy said as he got up to leave. "And I'll be back next week for the coat, for there's a lot of use left in it yet."

Mary rustled behind the sofa and went "Cluck, cluck."

"This time, by jakers, he'll have it," Tippitt told Sam as soon as Clancy had gone. "Get a move on there with your business, Mary."

When the chicks were hatched Tippitt gently moved them and thanked Mary kindly for her trouble. Then he carried the coat outside and spread it to air on the hawthorn hedge.

But when he went to take it in he saw that a pair of sparrows were building a nest right in the middle of it.

Tippitt scratched his head. "Well, there's not a soul with a drop of kindness that would disturb a pair of lovebirds when they're building their nest. Should we tell Clance what's going on with his coat, or should we try putting him off another time? I'll admit to something, Sam. I like having Clance around again. And I noticed the way his hands touched those carrots and leeks he brought over. He loves them, so he does. I should have tried harder to know how he felt when poor Bridget stepped all over his garden."

Sam nodded.

"You think I should tell him where the coat is, then?"

Sam nodded again.

When Clancy came he brought a bunch of new rhubarb, pink and tender.

"Isn't that the loveliest thing?" Tippitt said. "And inside there's some of Bridget's good cream to go along with it, sweet as sugar and thick enough to walk on. Now . . . about your coat . . ."

"It's finished?" Clancy asked, and Tippitt thought he looked somehow disappointed.

"Not so you'd notice," he replied. He took Clancy out and showed him the sparrow's nest.

"Aye, it's spring," Clancy said. "The hedge is in blossom and the birds are building. Let them be, Tippitt. Sure I've no need of the coat till winter, now, and you'll have it done by then."

"You're a reasonable man, Clance," Tippitt said, and Sam nodded—twice.

"Not all the time," Clancy said. "But a man learns. A garden comes back with care and attention. I thought maybe a friendship could too."

Tippitt smiled and put his arm around Clancy's shoulders. "You're right," he said. "Now wasn't it the luckiest thing, Clance, that your old coat needed turning?"

Clancy winked. "I told you there was a lot of use left in it."

Tippitt chuckled. "Well, I'll be jakered!"

😊 82

*Conjunction.* 1971. Romare Bearden.

Piquette. Photo: Estate of Romare Bearden

*Children Had Few Toys.* c. 1914–17
William Barnhill.

Silver gelatin print. Library of Congress.
Photo: PHOTRI

83 ❧

*The Good Friends.*
c. 1864. Honoré
Daumier.

Pencil, crayon, and watercolor,
9 1/4" x 11 7/8". George A. Lucas
Collection, Maryland Institute of Art,
Baltimore. On indefinite loan to The
Baltimore Museum of Art

# THE LEGEND OF DAMON AND PYTHIAS

adapted as a play by Fan Kissen

*illustrated by Rebecca Guay*

## CAST

| | |
|---|---|
| Damon | Second Robber |
| Pythias | First Voice |
| Soldier | Second Voice |
| King | Third Voice |
| Mother | Announcer |
| First Robber | Narrator |

## SOUNDS

*Iron door open and shut*      *Key in lock*

ANNOUNCER: Hello, listeners! It's story time again. Today's story is about the strong friendship between two men. Listen, and you'll hear how one of these men was ready to give up his life for his friend's sake.

MUSIC: (*Up full and out*)

NARRATOR: Long, long ago there lived on the island of Sicily two young men named Damon and Pythias. They were known far and wide for the strong friendship each had for the other. Their names have come down to our own times to mean true friendship. You may hear it said of two persons:

FIRST VOICE: Those two? Why, they're like Damon and Pythias!

NARRATOR: The King of that country was a cruel tyrant. He made cruel laws, and he showed no mercy toward anyone who broke his laws. Now, you might very well wonder:

SECOND VOICE: Why didn't the people rebel?

NARRATOR: Well, the people didn't dare rebel, because they feared the King's great and powerful army. No one dared say a word against the King or his laws—except Damon and Pythias. One day a soldier overheard Pythias speaking against a new law the King had proclaimed.

SOLDIER: Ho, there! Who are you, that dares to speak so about our King?

PYTHIAS: (*Unafraid*) I am called Pythias.

SOLDIER: Don't you know it is a crime to speak against

the King or his laws? You are under arrest! Come and tell this opinion of yours to the King's face!

MUSIC: (*A few short bars in and out*)

NARRATOR: When Pythias was brought before the King, he showed no fear. He stood straight and quiet before the throne.

KING: (*Hard, cruel*) So, Pythias! They tell me you do not approve of the laws I make.

PYTHIAS: I am not alone, your Majesty, in thinking your laws are cruel. But you rule the people with such an iron hand that they dare not complain.

KING: (*Angry*) But *you* have the daring to complain *for* them! Have they appointed you their champion?

PYTHIAS: No, your Majesty. I speak for myself alone. I have no wish to make trouble for anyone. But I am not afraid to tell you that the people are suffering under your rule. They want to have a voice in making the laws for themselves. You do not allow them to speak up for themselves.

KING: In other words, you are calling me a tyrant! Well, you shall learn for yourself how a tyrant treats a rebel! Soldier! Throw this man into prison!

SOLDIER: At once, your Majesty! Don't try to resist, Pythias!

PYTHIAS: I know better than to try to resist a soldier of the King! And for how long am I to remain in prison, your Majesty, merely for speaking out for the people?

KING: (*Cruel*) Not for very long, Pythias. Two weeks from today at noon, you shall be put to death in the public square, as an example to anyone else who may dare to question my laws or acts. Off to prison with him, soldier!

MUSIC: (*In briefly and out*)

NARRATOR: When Damon heard that his friend Pythias had been thrown into prison, and the severe punishment

that was to follow, he was heartbroken. He rushed to the prison and persuaded the guard to let him speak to his friend.

DAMON: Oh, Pythias! How terrible to find you here! I wish I could do something to save you!

PYTHIAS: Nothing can save me, Damon, my dear friend. I am prepared to die. But there is one thought that troubles me greatly.

DAMON: What is it? I will do anything to help you.

PYTHIAS: I'm worried about what will happen to my mother and my sister when I'm gone.

DAMON: I'll take care of them, Pythias, as if they were my own mother and sister.

PYTHIAS: Thank you, Damon. I have money to leave them. But there are other things I must arrange. If only I could go to see them before I die! But they live two days' journey from here, you know.

DAMON: I'll go to the King and beg him to give you your freedom for a few days. You'll give your word to return at the end of that time. Everyone in Sicily knows you for a man who has never broken his word.

PYTHIAS: Do you believe for one moment that the King would let me leave this prison, no matter how good my word may have been all my life?

DAMON: I'll tell him that *I* shall take your place in this prison cell. I'll tell him that if you do not return by the appointed day, he may kill *me*, in your place!

PYTHIAS: No, no, Damon! You must not do such a foolish thing! I cannot—I *will* not—let you do this! Damon! Damon! Don't go! (*To himself*) Damon, my friend! You may find yourself in a cell beside me!

MUSIC: (*In briefly and out*)

DAMON: (*Begging*) Your Majesty! I beg of you! Let Pythias go home for a few days to bid farewell to his mother and sister. He gives his word that he will return at your appointed time. Everyone knows that his word can be trusted.

KING: In ordinary business affairs—perhaps. But he is now a man under sentence of death. To free him even for a few days would strain his honesty—*any* man's honesty—too far. Pythias would never return here! I consider him a traitor, but I'm certain he's no fool.

DAMON: Your Majesty! I will take his place in the prison until he comes back. If he does not return, then you may take *my* life in his place.

KING: (*Astonished*) What did you say, Damon?

DAMON: I'm so certain of Pythias that I am offering to die in his place if he fails to return on time.

KING: I can't believe you mean it!

DAMON: I do mean it, your Majesty.

KING: You make me very curious, Damon, so curious that I'm willing to put you and Pythias to the test. This exchange of prisoners will be made. But Pythias must be back two weeks from today, at noon.

DAMON: Thank you, your Majesty!

KING: The order with my official seal shall go by your own hand, Damon. But I warn you, if your friend does not return on time, you shall surely die in his place! I shall show no mercy.

MUSIC: (*In briefly and out*)

NARRATOR: Pythias did not like the King's bargain with Damon. He did not like to leave his friend in prison, with the chance that he might lose his life if something went wrong. But at last Damon persuaded him to leave, and Pythias set out for his home. More than a week went by. The day set for the death sentence drew near. Pythias did not return. Everyone in the city knew of the condition on which the King had permitted Pythias to go home. Everywhere people met, the talk was sure to turn to the two friends.

FIRST VOICE: Do you suppose Pythias will come back?

SECOND VOICE: Why should he stick his head under the King's axe, once he's escaped?

THIRD VOICE: Still, would an honorable man like Pythias let such a good friend die for him?

FIRST VOICE: There's no telling what a man will do when it's a question of his own life against another's.

SECOND VOICE: But if Pythias doesn't come back before the time is up, he will be killing his friend.

THIRD VOICE: Well, there's still a few days' time. I, for one, am certain that Pythias *will* return in time.

SECOND VOICE: And *I* am just as certain that he will *not*. Friendship is friendship, but a man's own life is something stronger, *I* say!

NARRATOR: Two days before the time was up, the King himself visited Damon in his prison cell.

SOUND: (*Iron door unlocked and opened*)

KING: (*Mocking*) You see now, Damon, that you were a fool to make this bargain. Your friend has tricked you! He will not come back here to be killed! He has deserted you.

DAMON: (*Calm and firm*) I have faith in my friend. I know he will return.

KING: (*Mocking*) We shall see!

SOUND: (*Iron door shut and locked*)

NARRATOR: Meanwhile, when Pythias reached the home of his family he arranged his business affairs so that his mother and sister would be able to live comfortably for the rest of their years. Then he said a last farewell to them before starting back to the city.

MOTHER: (*In tears*) Pythias, it will take you only two days to get back. Stay another day, I beg you!

PYTHIAS: I dare not stay longer, Mother. Remember, Damon is locked up in my prison cell while I'm gone. Please don't make it any harder for me! Farewell! Don't weep for me. My death may help to bring better days for all our people.

NARRATOR: So Pythias began his journey in plenty of time. But bad luck struck him on the very first day.

92

At twilight, as he walked along a lonely stretch of woodland, a rough voice called:

FIRST ROBBER: Not so fast there, young man! Stop!

PYTHIAS: (*Startled*) Oh! What is it? What do you want?

SECOND ROBBER: Your money bags.

PYTHIAS: My money bags? I have only this small bag of coins. I shall need them for some favors, perhaps, before I die.

FIRST ROBBER: What do you mean, before you die? We don't mean to kill you, only take your money.

PYTHIAS: I'll give you my money, only don't delay me any longer. I am to die by the King's order three days from now. If I don't return to prison on time, my friend must die in my place.

FIRST ROBBER: A likely story! What man would be fool enough to go back to prison, ready to die.

SECOND ROBBER: And what man would be fool enough to die *for* you?

FIRST ROBBER: We'll take your money, all right. And we'll tie you up while we get away.

PYTHIAS: (*Begging*) No! No! I must get back to free my friend! (*Fade*) I must go back!

NARRATOR: But the two robbers took Pythias's money, tied him to a tree, and went off as fast as they could. Pythias struggled to free himself. He cried out for help as loud as he could, for a long time. But no one traveled through that lonesome woodland after dark. The sun had

been up for many hours before he finally managed to free himself from the ropes that had tied him to the tree. He lay on the ground, hardly able to breathe.

MUSIC: (*In briefly and out*)

NARRATOR: After a while Pythias got to his feet. Weak and dizzy from hunger and thirst and his struggle to free himself, he set off again. Day and night he traveled without stopping, desperately trying to reach the city in time to save Damon's life.

MUSIC: (*Up and out*)

NARRATOR: On the last day, half an hour before noon, Damon's hands were tied behind his back and he was taken into the public square. The people muttered angrily

as Damon was led in by the jailer. Then the King entered and seated himself on a high platform.

SOUND: (*Crowd voices in and hold under single voices*)

SOLDIER: (*Loud*) Long live the King!

FIRST VOICE: (*Low*) The longer he lives, the more miserable our lives will be!

KING: (*Loud, mocking*) Well, Damon, your lifetime is nearly up. Where is your good friend Pythias now?

DAMON: (*Firm*) I have faith in my friend. If he has not returned, I'm certain it is through no fault of his own.

KING: (*Mocking*) The sun is almost overhead. The shadow is almost at the noon mark. And still your friend has not returned to give you back your life!

DAMON: (*Quiet*) I am ready, and happy, to die in his place.

KING: (*Harsh*) And you shall, Damon! Jailer, lead the prisoner to the—

SOUND: (*Crowd voices up to a roar, then under*)

FIRST VOICE: (*Over noise*) Look! It's Pythias!

SECOND VOICE: (*Over noise*) Pythias has come back!

PYTHIAS: (*Breathless*) Let me through! Damon!

DAMON: Pythias!

PYTHIAS: Thank the gods I'm not too late!

DAMON: (*Quiet, sincere*) I would have died for you gladly, my friend.

CROWD VOICES: (*Loud, demanding*) Set them free! Set them both free!

KING: (*Loud*) People of the city! (*Crowd voices out*) Never in all my life have I seen such faith and friendship, such loyalty between men. There are many among you who call me harsh and cruel. But I cannot kill *any* man who proves such strong and true friendship for another. Damon and Pythias, I set you both free. (*Roar of approval from crowd*) I am King. I command a great army. I have stores of gold and precious jewels. But I would give all my money and power for one friend like Damon or Pythias.

SOUND: (*Roar of approval from crowd up briefly and out*)

MUSIC: (*Up and out*)

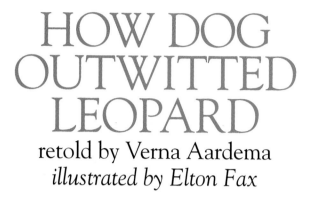

# HOW DOG OUTWITTED LEOPARD

retold by Verna Aardema
*illustrated by Elton Fax*

In the early days in Uganda, Dog and Leopard were friends. They lived together in a cave, sharing the work and sharing their food.

But Leopard was stronger and bolder than Dog, and a better hunter. Before long Dog began to grow fat on the game brought in by his partner. The fatter he grew, the lazier he became, until he stopped hunting altogether.

At first Dog tried to cover up his failure to bring home meat. He invented stories about wart hogs or rabbits which he had *almost* caught. After a time he decided he must think of a better way of deceiving his friend.

And he did.

One evening Leopard said, "I've been watching a black goat down in the village of people. I think it is fat enough for eating, and tonight I'm going to get it."

"Did you say a *black* goat?" asked Dog. "That's odd. I've had my eye on a black goat, too. I think I shall go hunting myself tonight."

The two friends slept until the darkest hour just before the dawn. Then they loped off to the village. They parted near the village fence, Dog going one way and Leopard the other.

Dog ran a little way, then retraced his steps and followed Leopard from a little distance.

Leopard picked his way along the fence until he came to a goat pen. Then he backed away, gave a run, and easily cleared the palings. He killed the black goat, flung it over his shoulder, and leaped back over the fence.

At that moment Dog beat the ground and the fence with a big stick. He changed his voice and shouted, "Leopard has stolen a goat! Catch him! Catch him! There he goes! Give me that spear!"

Leopard thought the whole village was after him. He dropped the goat and ran for his life.

Then Dog trotted over, picked up the goat, and dragged it home to the cave.

"Come and see my goat!" he called to Leopard. "Isn't it a fat one! Where's your goat?"

Leopard told him of his bad luck.

"What a shame!" said Dog. "You and I will share this one."

Leopard helped build a fire to cook the goat.

When the meat was almost ready, Dog slipped out of the cave. He ran to a place just out of sight of the entrance and began beating the ground with a stick. "Ou! Ou!" he shouted. "Don't kill me! It was Leopard who killed your goat! Ou! Ou! Ou!"

Back in the cave Leopard said to himself, "The men have tracked me to my den. They are killing Dog and they will kill me next." And off he streaked into the forest.

When Dog saw that his trick had worked, he went back into the cave and ate the goat all by himself.

At dusk Leopard returned and saw Dog lying all stretched out, too full of meat to move.

Dog moaned, "Don't touch me, my friend. Those men nearly killed me! In fact they left me for dead!"

"Poor fellow!" said Leopard. "Just lie there and rest. Nothing heals like a good rest. I'll fetch us another goat soon."

Two nights later, Leopard went hunting again. Dog sneaked after him and tricked him as before, bringing in the goat himself, and then eating it himself.

Leopard was very much embarrassed by his failures. He still hadn't caught on to Dog's treachery. He decided to seek help from Muzimu, the spirit of the forest.

He found Muzimu deep in the heart of the jungle where vines coil around the trees and hang in long loops over a little black pool.

Leopard called into the pool. "Oh, Muzimu, have pity on me! Once I was a matchless hunter. Now I am dying of hunger. Though I still catch my prey, I am always driven away from it. Tell me, Muzimu, how my good luck may return."

Leopard listened. From deep down in the pool came a faint voice.

"Watch Dog. You know how to catch prey. Dog knows how to eat it. Watch Dog!"

Leopard couldn't understand how watching his friend would make his good luck return, but he decided to follow the advice.

The next night Leopard said, "I have spotted a tan goat that looks good to me. I am going to try to get it and *keep* it, this time."

"A *tan* goat?" said Dog. "I know where there are some tan goats, too. I think I'll go hunting with you tonight."

The two traveled together to the edge of the village, then separated just as before.

Leopard leaped over the fence near the goat pen, killed a tan goat, and leaped back over the palings with it.

Dog, who was hiding nearby, began threshing about, beating the fence and calling out in a strange voice. "Leopard has stolen a goat! Kill him!"

This time Leopard did not run away. He ran toward the commotion. Then he saw Dog's ears sticking up above the tall grass.

Suddenly Leopard knew who had been frightening him! With a snarl he lunged after Dog.

Round and round the village, Dog ran for his life. At last he found an opening under the fence and squeezed through just in time.

In his terror he streaked across a garden and straight into the hut of a man.

The man leaped out of bed, caught up his spear, and was about to kill Dog. But that clever creature crouched low with his head between his forepaws and his tail wagging furiously. He cocked his head and looked into Man's face. He whimpered softly, and Man understood that all he wanted was to be his friend.

And to this day, Man and Dog are fast friends, but Leopard and Dog are sworn enemies.

## MEET VERNA AARDEMA, AUTHOR

*". . . it was my little daughter who got me started writing children's stories. She wouldn't eat without a story. And she could make a scrambled egg last all the way through 'Little Red Riding Hood.' After a time, I began to make up little feeding stories. That way she didn't know how far off the end would be. Because I was usually reading about Africa, the feeding stories were apt to be set in Ashantiland or the Kalahari Desert."*

103

## MEET ELTON FAX, ILLUSTRATOR

*As a child, Elton Fax borrowed books often from the public library. He particularly enjoyed the classic fairy tales "so beautifully illustrated in pen and ink and in color." But his special favorites were a series of travel books for children called Our Little Cousins. He says, "How I enjoyed reading about our little cousins from far off and often exotic lands—Armenia, Bolivia, Latvia, Georgia, Kenya, Argentina, Uruguay, Italy, Uganda, Ethiopia, Nigeria. . . . How little indeed did I ever dream I would not only visit such places but that I would be making drawings in them and later writing about them so that others could share what I have seen and heard and felt."*

# TEAMMATES

Peter Golenbock

*illustrated by Paul Bacon*

Jackie Robinson

Pee Wee Reese

*Jackie Robinson was more than just my teammate.*
*He had a tremendous amount of talent, ability, and dedication.*
*Jackie set a standard for future generations of ball players.*
*He was a winner. Jackie Robinson was also a man.*

—PEE WEE REESE
*October 31, 1989*

Once upon a time in America, when automobiles were black and looked like tanks and laundry was white and hung on clotheslines to dry, there were two wonderful baseball leagues that no longer exist. They were called the Negro Leagues.

The Negro Leagues had extraordinary players, and adoring fans came to see them wherever they played. They were heroes, but players in the Negro Leagues didn't make much money and their lives on the road were hard.

Laws against segregation didn't exist in the 1940s. In many places in this country, black people were not allowed to go to the same schools and churches as white people. They couldn't sit in the front of a bus or trolley car. They couldn't drink from the same drinking fountains that white people drank from.

Back then, many hotels didn't rent rooms to black people, so the Negro League players slept in their cars.

Satchel Paige
The National Baseball Hall of Fame

Many towns had no restaurants that would serve them, so they often had to eat meals that they could buy and carry with them.

Life was very different for the players in the Major Leagues. They were the leagues for white players. Compared to the Negro League players, white players were very well paid. They stayed in good hotels and ate in fine restaurants. Their pictures were put on baseball cards and the best players became famous all over the world.

Many Americans knew that racial prejudice was wrong, but few dared to challenge openly the way things were. And many people were apathetic about racial problems. Some feared that it could be dangerous to object. Vigilante groups, like the Ku Klux Klan, reacted violently against those who tried to change the way blacks were treated.

The general manager of the Brooklyn Dodgers baseball team was a man by the name of Branch

Branch Rickey
The National Baseball
Hall of Fame

Rickey. He was not afraid of change. He wanted to treat the Dodger fans to the best players he could find, regardless of the color of their skin. He thought segregation was unfair and wanted to give everyone, regardless of race or creed, an opportunity to compete equally on ballfields across America.

To do this, the Dodgers needed one special man.

Branch Rickey launched a search for him. He was looking for a star player in the Negro Leagues who would be able to compete successfully despite threats on his life or attempts to injure him. He would have to possess the self-control not to fight back when opposing players tried to intimidate or hurt him. If this man disgraced himself on the field, Rickey knew, his opponents would use it as an excuse to keep blacks out of Major League baseball for many more years.

Rickey thought Jackie Robinson might be just the man.

Jackie rode the train to Brooklyn to meet Mr. Rickey. When Mr. Rickey told him, "I want a man with the courage not to fight back," Jackie Robinson replied, "If you take this gamble, I will do my best to perform." They shook hands. Branch Rickey and Jackie Robinson were starting on what would be known in history as "the great experiment."

AP/Wide World

At spring training with the Dodgers, Jackie was mobbed by blacks, young and old, as if he were a savior. He was the first black player to try out for a Major League team. If he succeeded, they knew, others would follow.

Initially, life with the Dodgers was for Jackie a series of humiliations. The players on his team who came from the South, men who had been taught to avoid black people since childhood, moved to another table whenever he sat down next to them.

Many opposing players were cruel to him, calling him nasty names from their dugouts. A few tried to hurt him with their spiked shoes. Pitchers aimed at his head. And he received threats on his life, both from individuals and from organizations like the Ku Klux Klan.

Despite all the difficulties, Jackie Robinson didn't give up. He made the Brooklyn Dodgers team.

But making the Dodgers was only the beginning. Jackie had to face abuse and hostility throughout the season, from April through September. His worst pain was inside. Often he felt very alone. On the road he had to live by himself, because only the white players were allowed in the hotels in towns where the team played.

The whole time Pee Wee Reese, the Dodger shortstop, was growing up in Louisville, Kentucky, he had rarely even seen a black person, unless it was in the back of a bus. Most of his friends and relatives hated the idea of his playing on the same field as a black man. In addition, Pee Wee Reese had more to lose than the other players when Jackie joined the team.

Jackie had been a shortstop, and everyone thought that Jackie would take Pee Wee's job. Lesser men might have felt anger toward Jackie, but Pee Wee was different. He told himself, "If he's good enough to take my job, he deserves it."

When his Southern teammates circulated a petition to throw Jackie off the team and asked him to sign it, Pee Wee responded, "I don't care if this man is black, blue or

striped"—and refused to sign. "He can play and he can help us win," he told the others. "That's what counts."

Very early in the season, the Dodgers traveled west to Ohio to play the Cincinnati Reds. Cincinnati is near Pee Wee's hometown of Louisville.

The Reds played in a small ballpark where the fans sat close to the field. The players could almost feel the breath of the fans on the backs of their necks. Many who came that day screamed terrible, hateful things at Jackie when the Dodgers were on the field.

More than anything else, Pee Wee Reese believed in doing what was right. When he heard the fans yelling at Jackie, Pee Wee decided to take a stand.

With his head high, Pee Wee walked directly from his shortstop position to where Jackie was playing first base.

The taunts and shouting of the fans were ringing in Pee Wee's ears. It saddened him, because he knew it could have been his friends and neighbors. Pee Wee's legs felt heavy, but he knew what he had to do.

As he walked toward Jackie wearing the gray Dodger uniform, he looked into his teammate's bold, pained eyes. The first baseman had done nothing to provoke the hostility except that he sought to be treated as an equal. Jackie was grim with anger. Pee Wee smiled broadly as he reached Jackie. Jackie smiled back.

Stopping beside Jackie, Pee Wee put his arm around Jackie's shoulders. An audible gasp rose up from the crowd when they saw what Pee Wee had done. Then there was silence.

Outlined on a sea of green grass stood these two great athletes, one black, one white, both wearing the same team uniform.

"I am standing by him," Pee Wee Reese said to the world. "This man is my teammate."

# BIBLIOGRAPHY

*Amos & Boris* by William Steig.
What do a mouse and a whale have in
common? Not much! But they become
the best of friends and do what good
friends should.

*Captain Snap and the Children
of Vinegar Lane* by Roni Schotter.
The children of Vinegar Lane befriend the
crabby old Captain Snap when he is ill.
What secret does their act of friendship
help to uncover?

*Ellen Tebbits* by Beverly Cleary.
Ellen Tebbits gains a best friend when she
discovers she shares the same secret with
Austine Allen, the new girl in school.

*Georgia to Georgia: Making Friends
in the U.S.S.R.* by Laurie Dolphin.
A young boy from Atlanta, Georgia, visits
the former Soviet Republic of Georgia
with his family to promote friendship and
understanding between the people of
both countries.

*Molly's Pilgrim* by Barbara Cohen. The children at school make fun of Molly, a Russian immigrant, when Molly's mother makes an unusual-looking Pilgrim doll for Molly's homework assignment.

*My First American Friend* by Sarunna Jin. The author of this book is a third-grader who tells her own story of adjusting to a new life in America with the help of her first American friend. With this book, Jin won Raintree's Heritage Publish-A-Book Contest, 1990.

*Twenty Ways to Lose Your Best Friend* by Marilyn Singer. Emma finds a new best friend and then loses her when she votes for someone else for the lead in the class play.

*Wilfred Gordon McDonald Partridge* by Mem Fox. A small boy asks "What's a memory?" in hopes of helping a special friend find hers.

# IMAGINATION

# THE BLIND MEN AND THE ELEPHANT

John Godfrey Saxe
*illustrated by Krystyna Stasiak*

It was six men of Indostan
    To learning much inclined,
Who went to see the Elephant
    (Though all of them were blind),
That each by observation
    Might satisfy his mind.

The First approached the Elephant,
    And happening to fall
Against his broad and sturdy side,
    At once began to bawl:
"Bless me! but the Elephant
    Is very like a wall!"

The Second, feeling of the tusk,
    Cried, "Ho! what have we here,
So very round and smooth and sharp?
    To me 'tis mighty clear
This wonder of an Elephant
    Is very like a spear!"

117

The Third approached the animal,
    And happening to take
The squirming trunk within his hands,
    Thus boldly up and spake:
"I see," quoth he, "the Elephant
    Is very like a snake!"

The Fourth reached out his eager hand,
    And felt about the knee.
"What most this wondrous beast is like
    Is mighty plain," quoth he;
" 'Tis clear enough the Elephant
    Is very like a tree!"

The Fifth, who chanced to touch the ear,
    Said, "E'en the blindest man
Can tell what this resembles most;
    Deny the fact who can,
This marvel of an Elephant
    Is very like a fan!"

The Sixth no sooner had begun
    About the beast to grope,
Than, seizing on the swinging tail
    That fell within his scope,
"I see," quoth he, "the Elephant
    Is very like a rope!"

119

And so these men of Indostan
  Disputed loud and long,
Each in his own opinion
  Exceeding stiff and strong,
Though each was partly in the right,
  And all were in the wrong!

# THROUGH GRANDPA'S EYES

Patricia MacLachlan

*illustrated by Deborah Ray*

Of all the houses that I know, I like my grandpa's best. My friend Peter has a new glass house with pebble-path gardens that go nowhere. And Maggie lives next door in an old wooden house with rooms behind rooms, all with carved doors and brass doorknobs. They are fine houses. But Grandpa's house is my favorite. Because I see it through Grandpa's eyes.

Grandpa is blind. He doesn't see the house the way I do. He has his own way of seeing.

In the morning, the sun pushes through the curtains into my eyes. I burrow down into the covers to get away, but the light follows me. I give up, throw back the covers, and run to Grandpa's room.

The sun wakes Grandpa differently from the way it wakes me. He says it touches him, warming him awake. When I peek around the door, Grandpa is already up and doing his morning exercises. Bending and stretching by the bed. He stops and smiles because he hears me.

"Good morning, John."

"Where's Nana?" I ask him.

"Don't you know?" he says, bending and stretching. "Close your eyes, John, and look through my eyes."

I close my eyes. Down below, I hear the banging of pots and the sound of water running that I didn't hear before.

"Nana is in the kitchen, making breakfast," I say.

When I open my eyes again, I can see Grandpa nodding at me. He is tall with dark gray hair. And his eyes are sharp blue even though they are not sharp seeing.

I exercise with Grandpa. Up and down. Then I try to exercise with my eyes closed.

"One, two," says Grandpa, "three, four."

"Wait!" I cry. I am still on one, two when Grandpa is on three, four.

I fall sideways. Three times. Grandpa laughs as he hears my thumps on the carpet.

"Breakfast!" calls Nana from downstairs.

"I smell eggs frying," says Grandpa. He bends his head close to mine. "And buttered toast."

The wooden banister on the stairway has been worn smooth from Grandpa running his fingers up and down. I walk behind him, my fingers following Grandpa's smooth path.

We go into the kitchen.

"I smell flowers," says Grandpa.

"What flowers?" I ask.

He smiles. He loves guessing games.

"Not violets, John, not peonies . . ."

"Carnations!" I cry. I love guessing games.

"Silly." Grandpa laughs. "Marigolds. Right, Nana?"

Nana laughs, too.

"That's too easy," she says, putting two plates of food in front of us.

"It's not too easy," I protest. "How can Grandpa tell? All the smells mix together in the air."

"Close your eyes, John," says Nana. "Tell me what breakfast is."

"I smell the eggs. I smell the toast," I say, my eyes closed. "And something else. The something else doesn't smell good."

"That something else," says Nana, smiling, "is the marigolds."

When he eats, Grandpa's plate of food is a clock.

"Two eggs at nine o'clock and toast at two o'clock," says Nana to Grandpa. "And a dollop of jam."

"A dollop of jam," I tell Grandpa, "at six o'clock."

I make my plate of food a clock, too, and eat through Grandpa's eyes.

After breakfast, I follow Grandpa's path through the dining room to the living room, to the window that he opens to feel the weather outside, to the table where he finds his pipe, and to his cello in the corner.

"Will you play with me, John?" he asks.

123

He tunes our cellos without looking. I play with a music stand and music before me. I know all about sharps and flats. I see them on the music. But Grandpa plays them. They are in his fingers. For a moment I close my eyes and play through Grandpa's eyes. My fingering hand slides up and down the cello neck—toward the pegs for flats, toward the bridge for sharps. But with my eyes closed my bow falls from the strings.

"Listen," says Grandpa. "I'll play a piece I learned when I was your age. It was my favorite."

He plays the tune while I listen. That is the way Grandpa learns new pieces. By listening.

"Now," says Grandpa. "Let's do it together."

"That's fine," says Grandpa as we play. "But C sharp, John," he calls to me. "C sharp!"

Later, Nana brings out her clay to sculpt my Grandpa's head.

"Sit still," she grumbles.

"I won't," he says, imitating her grumbly voice, making us laugh.

While she works, Grandpa takes out his piece of wood. He holds it when he's thinking. His fingers move back and forth across the wood, making smooth paths like the ones on the stair banister.

"Can I have a piece of thinking wood, too?" I ask.

Grandpa reaches in his shirt pocket and tosses a small bit of wood in my direction. I catch it. It is smooth with no splinters.

125

"The river is up," says Nana.

Grandpa nods a short nod. "It rained again last night. Did you hear the gurgling in the rain gutter?"

As they talk, my fingers begin a river on my thinking wood. The wood will winter in my pocket so when I am not at Grandpa's house I can still think about Nana, Grandpa, and the river.

When Nana is finished working, Grandpa runs his hand over the sculpture, his fingers soft and quick like butterflies.

"It looks like me," he says, surprised.

My eyes have already told me that it looks like Grandpa. But he shows me how to feel his face with my three middle fingers, and then the clay face.

"Pretend your fingers are water," he tells me.

My waterfall fingers flow down his clay head, filling in the spaces beneath the eyes like little pools before they flow down over the cheeks. It does feel like Grandpa. This time my fingers tell me.

Grandpa and I walk outside, through the front yard and across the field to the river. Grandpa has not been blind forever. He remembers in his mind the gleam of the sun on the river, the Queen Anne's lace in the meadow, and every dahlia in his garden. But he gently takes my elbow as we walk so that I can help show him the path.

"I feel a south wind," says Grandpa.

I can tell which way the wind is blowing because I see the way the tops of the trees lean. Grandpa tells by the feel of the meadow grasses and by the way his hair blows against his face.

When we come to the riverbank, I see that Nana was right. The water is high and has cut in by the willow tree. It flows around and among the roots of the tree, making paths. Paths like Grandpa's on the stair banister and on the thinking wood. I see a blackbird with a red patch on its wing sitting on a cattail. Without thinking, I point my finger.

"What is that bird, Grandpa?" I asked excitedly.

"Conk-a-ree," the bird calls to us.

"A red-winged blackbird," says Grandpa promptly.

He can't see my finger pointing. But he hears the song of the bird.

"And somewhere behind the blackbird," he says listening, "a song sparrow."

I hear a scratchy song, and I look and look until I see the earth-colored bird that Grandpa knows is here.

Nana calls from the front porch of the house.

"Nana's made hot bread for lunch," he tells me happily. "And spice tea." Spice tea is his favorite.

I close my eyes, but all I can smell is the wet earth by the river.

As we walk back to the house, Grandpa stops suddenly. He bends his head to one side, listening. He points his finger upward.

"Honkers," he whispers.

I look up and see a flock of geese, high in the clouds, flying in a V.

"Canada geese," I tell him.

"Honkers," he insists. And we both laugh.

We walk up the path again and to the yard where Nana is painting the porch chairs. Grandpa smells the paint.

"What color, Nana?" he asks. "I cannot smell the color."

"Blue," I tell him, smiling. "Blue like the sky."

"Blue like the color of Grandpa's eyes," Nana says.

When he was younger, before I can remember, before he was blind, Grandpa did things the way I do. Now, when we drink tea and eat lunch on the porch, Grandpa pours his own cup of tea by putting his finger just inside the rim of the cup to tell him when it is full. He never burns his finger. Afterward, when I wash the dishes, he feels them as he dries them. He even sends some back for me to wash again.

"Next time," says Grandpa, pretending to be cross, "I wash, you dry."

In the afternoon, Grandpa, Nana, and I take our books outside to read under the apple tree. Grandpa reads his book with his fingers, feeling the raised Braille dots that tell him the words.

As he reads, Grandpa laughs out loud.

"Tell us what's funny," says Nana. "Read to us, Papa."

And he does.

Nana and I put down our books to listen. A gray squirrel comes down the trunk of the apple tree, tail high, and seems to listen, too. But Grandpa doesn't see him.

After supper, Grandpa turns on the television. I watch, but Grandpa listens, and the music and the words tell him when something is dangerous or funny, happy or sad.

Somehow, Grandpa knows when it is dark, and he takes me upstairs and tucks me into bed. He bends down to kiss me, his hands feeling my head.

"You need a haircut, John," he says.

Before Grandpa leaves, he pulls the light chain above my bed to turn out the light. But, by mistake, he's turned it on instead. I lie for a moment after he's gone, smiling, before I get up to turn off the light.

Then, when it is dark for me the way it is dark for Grandpa, I hear the night noises that Grandpa hears. The house creaking, the birds singing their last songs of the day, the wind rustling the tree outside my window.

Then, all of a sudden, I hear the sounds of geese overhead. They fly low over the house.

"Grandpa," I call softly, hoping he's heard them too.

"Honkers," he calls back.

"Go to sleep, John," says Nana.

Grandpa says her voice smiles to him. I test it.

"What?" I call to her.

"I said go to sleep," she answers.

She says it sternly. But Grandpa is right. Her voice smiles to me. I know. Because I'm looking through Grandpa's eyes.

131

132

The Apple
      is on the top
branch
    of the tree
        touching
the
sky
    or the apple is
        in
    the
    sky
touching
    the top branch
      of the tree
and i am
    me on the ground
    waiting
      for
        a
    good
    wind

—Arnold Adoff

*illustrated by Paul Hoffman*

# HOUSES

Houses are faces
(haven't you found?)
with their hats in the air,
and their necks in the ground.

Windows are noses,
windows are eyes,
and doors are the mouths
of a suitable size.

And a porch—or the place
where porches begin—
is just like a mustache
shading the chin.

—Aileen Fisher

# FOG

The fog comes
on little cat feet.

It sits looking
over harbor and city
on silent haunches
and then moves on.

—Carl Sandburg

133

# THE CAT WHO BECAME A POET

Margaret Mahy

*illustrated by Quentin Blake*

A cat once caught a mouse, as cats do.

"Don't eat me," cried the mouse. "I am a poet with a poem to write."

"That doesn't make any difference to me," replied the cat. "It is a rule that cats must eat mice, and that is all there is to it."

"If only you'd listen to my poem you'd feel differently about it all," said the mouse.

"Okay," yawned the cat, "I don't mind hearing a poem, but I warn you, it won't make any difference."

So the mouse danced and sang:

"The great mouse Night with the starry tail
Slides over the hills and trees,
Eating the crumbs in the corners of Day
And nibbling the moon like cheese."

"Very good! That's very good!" the cat said. "But a poem is only a poem and cats still eat mice."

And he ate the mouse, as cats do.

Then he washed his paws and his face and curled up in a bed of catnip, tucking in his nose and his tail and his paws. Then he had a little cat nap.

Some time later he woke up in alarm.

"What's wrong with me?" he thought. "I feel so strange." He felt as if his head was full of colored lights. Pictures came and went behind his eyes. Things that were different seemed alike. Things that were real changed and became dreams.

135

"Horrakapotchkin!" thought the cat. "I want to write a poem."

He opened his mouth to meow, but a poem came out instead:

> "The great Sun-Cat comes up in the east.
> Lo! The glory of his whiskers touches the hills.
> Behold! the fire of his smiling
> Burns on the oceans of the rolling world."

"Cat-curses!" said the cat to himself. "I have turned into a poet, but I don't want to make poetry. I just want to be a cat catching mice and sleeping in the catnip bed. I will have to ask the witch about this."

The cat went to the witch's crooked house. The witch sat at the window with her head in her hands. Her dreams turned into black butterflies and flew out of the window.

She took the cat's temperature and gave him some magic medicine that tasted of dandelions.

"Now talk!" she commanded.

The cat opened his mouth to ask her if he was cured. Instead he found himself saying:

> "Lying in the catnip bed,
> The flowering cherry over my head,
> Am I really the cat that I seem?
> Or only a cat in another cat's dream?"

"I'm afraid it is too late," said the witch. "Your case is hopeless. Poetry has got into your blood and you're stuck with it for the rest of your life."

"Horrakapotchkin!" cried the cat sadly, and he started off home.

But, five houses away from his own house, a black dog called Max chased him, as dogs do, and the cat had to run up a tree. He boxed with his paw at Max and went to hiss and spit at him, but instead he found himself saying:

"Colonel Dog fires his cannon
And puts his white soldiers on parade.
He guards the house from cats, burglars
And any threat of peacefulness."

The dog Max stopped and stared. "What did you call me?
Colonel Dog? I like that. But what do you mean, I fire my
cannon?"

"That's your barking," said the cat.

"And what do you mean, I put my white soldiers on parade?" asked the dog again.

"That's your teeth," said the cat.

The dog wagged his tail. "I like the way you put it," he said again. "How did you learn to talk like that?"

"Oh, it's poetry," said the cat carelessly. "I am a poet, you see."

"Well, I'll tell you what! I'll let you go without barking at you if I may come and hear that poem again sometimes," the dog Max said, still wagging his tail. "Perhaps I could bring some other dogs to hear it too. Colonel Dog, eh? White soldiers, eh? Very true." And he let the cat go on home to his catnip bed.

"If only he knew," the cat thought. "I wasn't meaning to praise him. Poetry is very tricky stuff and can be taken two ways."

The cat went on thinking. "I became a poet through eating the mouse. Perhaps the mouse became a poet through eating seeds. Perhaps all this poetry stuff is just the world's way of talking about itself." And straight away he felt another poem coming into his mind.

"Just time for a sleep first," he muttered into his whiskers. "One thing, I'll never eat another poet again. One is quite enough." And he curled up in the catnip bed for a quick kip-and-catnap, as cats do.

Let's get to the next page before he wakes up...

# PICASSO
## Mike Venezia

AP/Wide World

Pablo Picasso was one of the greatest artists of the twentieth century. He was born in Malaga, Spain, in 1881, and died in France in 1973.

Picasso's father was an art teacher at the local school. He encouraged his son to paint and draw. He wanted Picasso to become a great artist some day.

Picasso's painting style changed more over the period of his life than any other great artist. He was always trying new and different things.

140

The painting at the right was done when he was only fifteen years old.

*Portrait of Dora Maar.* 1937. Pablo Picasso.

Oil on canvas. Musée Picasso, Paris. ©1994 ARS, NY/SPADEM, Paris.
Photo: SCALA/Art Resource

*Portrait of the Artist's Mother (Maria Picasso Lopez).* 1896. Pablo Picasso.

Oil on canvas. Museo Picasso, Barcelona. ©1994 ARS, NY/SPADEM, Paris. Photo: Giraudon/Art Resource

141 ❦

This painting was done when Picasso was fifty-six.

There's quite a difference between the two paintings, isn't there?

*Le Moulin de la Galette*. Autumn 1900. Pablo Picasso.

Oil on canvas. Gift of Justin K. Thannhauser Collection, 1978, Solomon R. Guggenheim Museum. ©1994 ARS, NY/SPADEM, Paris. Photo: David Heald ©The Solomon R. Guggenheim Foundation, New York

When Picasso was nineteen, he left Spain and went to Paris, France. Some of the first paintings he did there look a little bit like the work of other famous French artists.

This painting reminds many people of the work done by Toulouse-Lautrec. Some of Picasso's other early paintings remind people of Van Gogh, Gauguin, and Monet.

## THE BLUE PERIOD

Then something happened! Picasso's paintings changed. His work became different from anyone else's.

His best friend died, and Picasso felt alone and sad. At the same time, none of his paintings were selling, and he was almost starving to death.

Because of his mood, Picasso began to paint with lots of blue (blue can be a very sad color). He made all the people in his paintings look lonely and sad.

Some people thought Picasso's blue paintings were great. Others (including Picasso's father) thought they were just too strange. This meant his paintings were controversial.

*The Old Guitarist.* 1903. Pablo Picasso.

Oil on panel, 122.9 x 82.6 cm. Helen Birch Bartlett Memorial Collection, The Art Institute of Chicago. 1926.253. ©1994 ARS, NY/SPADEM, Paris. Photo: ©1992 The Art Institute of Chicago. All Rights Reserved

143

Picasso's Blue Period ended when he met a girl named Fernande. Fernande and Picasso fell in love, and soon a happier color started showing up in Picasso's paintings. This was the beginning of the Rose Period.

Not only were Picasso's colors happier during the Rose Period, but he started painting happier things. Picasso painted a lot of circus people during this time. He often painted them with their animals.

 *144*

The Rose Period didn't last very long, though, because Picasso found a new way to paint that was really exciting and different.

*Family of Saltimbanques.* 1905.
Pablo Picasso.

Oil on canvas. Chester Dale Collection, National Gallery of Art. ©1994 ARS, NY/SPADEM, Paris. Photo: ©National Gallery of Art, Washington

## CUBISM

Cubism was the next style of painting that Picasso developed and made famous.

This is a cubist painting of one of Picasso's friends. The man in the painting looks like he's been broken up into little cubes. That's where the name cubism came from.

Look closely. Can you see the man's face, what he was wearing, his hands, a bottle, a glass, and maybe his pet cat? Can you find anything else?

Cubism is one of the most important periods in the history of modern art.

For hundreds of years, artists tried very hard to paint things so they would look real. Then Picasso came along and started to paint people and things that didn't look the way people and things were supposed to look.

Picasso was always shocking people, but when he started painting people who had eyes and noses in the wrong places —well, even some of his closest friends thought he had gone too far.

*Portrait of Daniel-Henry Kahnweiler.* 1910. Pablo Picasso.

*Three Musicians*. Fontainebleau, Summer 1921. Pablo Picasso.
Oil on canvas, 6'7" x 7'3 3/4". Mrs. Simon Guggenheim Fund, The Museum of Modern Art, New York.
©1994 ARS, NY/SPADEM, Paris

Picasso kept working with cubism and changed it over the years. It became much more colorful and flatter looking. It also became easier to see what Picasso was painting.

In the painting *Three Musicians*, you can see the three musicians, and tell what instruments they're playing.

In another style that popped up for a while, Picasso painted people who looked more real again. Picasso had just visited Rome, a city filled with statues and monuments. When he returned from his trip, he did a series of paintings in which people look like they've been chiseled out of stone, like statues.

Many of Picasso's paintings look funny because of the way he moves eyes, noses, and chins around. The amazing thing about these paintings is how much they look like the real person.

Look at the painting below of Picasso's best friend, Jaime Sabartés. Does it look like the same man shown in the smaller painting to the right?

The thing that made Picasso such a great artist was his originality. He had the imagination to try new and different things through his entire life.

*Portrait of Jaime Sabartés as a Spanish Grandee.* 1939. Pablo Picasso.

Oil on canvas. Museo Picasso, Barcelona. ©1994 ARS, NY/SPADEM, Paris

Jaime Sabartés, painted by
Steve Dobson, from a photograph
by Gilberte Brassai

*Portrait of Aunt Pepa.* c. 1895–96. Pablo Picasso.
Museo Picasso, Barcelona. ©1994 ARS, NY/SPADEM, Paris. Photo: Giraudon/Art Resource

*Ape and Her Child.* 1952. Pablo Picasso.
Bronze. Musée Picasso, Paris. ©1994 ARS, NY/SPADEM,
Paris. Photo: Giraudon/Art Resource

*Weeping Woman.* 1937. Pablo Picasso.

Oil on canvas. Private collection. ©1994 ARS,
NY/SPADEM, Paris. Photo: The Bridgeman Art
Library/Art Resource

Picasso lived to be ninety-two years old. He was a great painter, but he was great at other things, too.

He made sculptures, prints, drawings, beautifully colored dishes and bowls. He even made costumes and scenery for plays.

It's a lot of fun to see real Picasso paintings. You'll be surprised at how big some of them are. Look for his paintings in your art museum.

Most of the pictures in this biography came from the museums listed below. If none of these museums is close to you, maybe you can visit one when you are on vacation.

The Museum of Modern Art, New York, New York
Solomon R. Guggenheim Museum, New York, New York
The Art Institute, Chicago, Illinois
National Gallery of Art, Washington, D. C.
Picasso Museum, Barcelona, Spain
Musée Picasso, Paris, France

149

MEET MIKE VENEZIA, AUTHOR AND ILLUSTRATOR
*Mike Venezia studied art at the School of the Art Institute in Chicago. He thinks the best way for children to learn about art and artists is through fun. "If children can look at art in a fun way, and think of artists as real people, the exciting world of art will be open to them for the rest of their lives."*

# FINE ART
## IMAGINATION

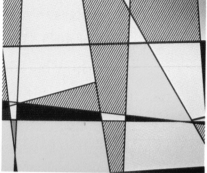

*Cow Triptych.* 1974. Roy Lichtenstein.

Oil tempera on canvas, 3 panels, each 68" x 62". ©Roy Lichtenstein. Photo: Leo Castelli Gallery, New York

150

*The Sun of Paris.* 1975. Marc Chagall.

Oil on canvas. Artist's collection, St. Paul de Vence.
©1994 ARS, NY/ADAGP, Paris.
Photo: SCALA/Art Resource

*Time Transfixed.* 1938.
René Magritte.

Oil on canvas, 146.1 x 97.5 cm. Joseph Winterbotham
Collection, The Art Institute of Chicago.

151 ❧

*The Desk. July 1st,
1984.* David
Hockney.

Photographic collage,
48 1/2" x 46 1/2".
Collection of the artist.
©David Hockney

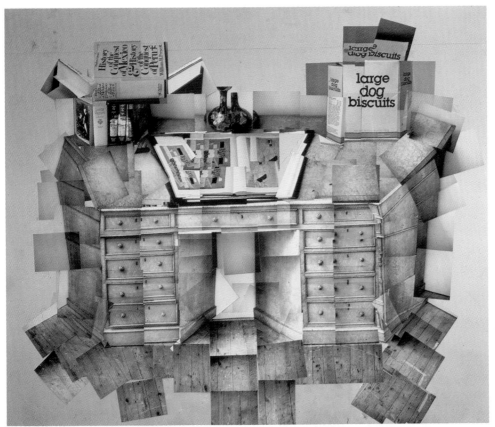

*Self-Portrait.* 1514. Leonardo da Vinci.

Red chalk on paper. Biblioteca Reale, Torino, Italy

# THE INCREDIBLE LEONARDO DA VINCI

Robert Ross and Martin Woodhouse

Incredible? You decide.

Leonardo da Vinci designed a workable parachute. The hang glider. A spring-driven automobile. The submarine. A deep-sea diving suit. Yet he lived more than half a *thousand* years ago!

Leonardo was born on 15 April 1452 in the tiny hillside village of Vinci in Italy. It was a very long time ago, and we know almost nothing of his youth or his family. One of his biographers—an artist named Vasari—tells us that Leonardo gained great fame when he was young. Leonardo, he wrote, was handsome and brave and so strong, he could straighten a horseshoe with his bare hands!

Was it true? Vasari may have been seven or eight years old when Leonardo died in 1519. The biography, therefore, was written many years later and may have been based on gossip or hearsay.

But never mind. We have Leonardo's *Notebooks*.

He must have started to write his ideas down in his *Notebooks* when still a young man. He filled perhaps forty

153

thousand pages with his visions, his questions, his inventions. Five thousand of those pages somehow survived the centuries, and they tell us a great deal about Leonardo.

History gives the Italian astronomer Galileo the credit for inventing the telescope. Yet in Leonardo's *Notebooks* we find his design for a working two-power telescope one hundred years before Galileo!

Leonardo da Vinci was the first to draw an exact picture of the unborn infant curled in its mother's womb.

He invented new musical instruments, the portable bridge, the river dredger, a twelve-hour clock. He designed pulleys and gears, brakes and couplings, grinders and valves—and the sort of linked chain you see on modern bicycles.

On page after page of the *Notebooks* we can find his drawings and designs about chemistry, physics, biology, botany, hydraulics, astronomy, metallurgy, architecture, city planning—all carefully described in mysterious "mirror writing."

To read this writing, you have to hold the page up to a mirror and read the reflection in the glass! Leonardo, you see, wrote backwards, from right to left. For centuries men thought his writing was some sort of code. Today, we are almost certain that he had a form of dyslexia (or reading problem), so that the message centers of his brain did not work normally. And so he wrote in mirror writing. With his left hand.

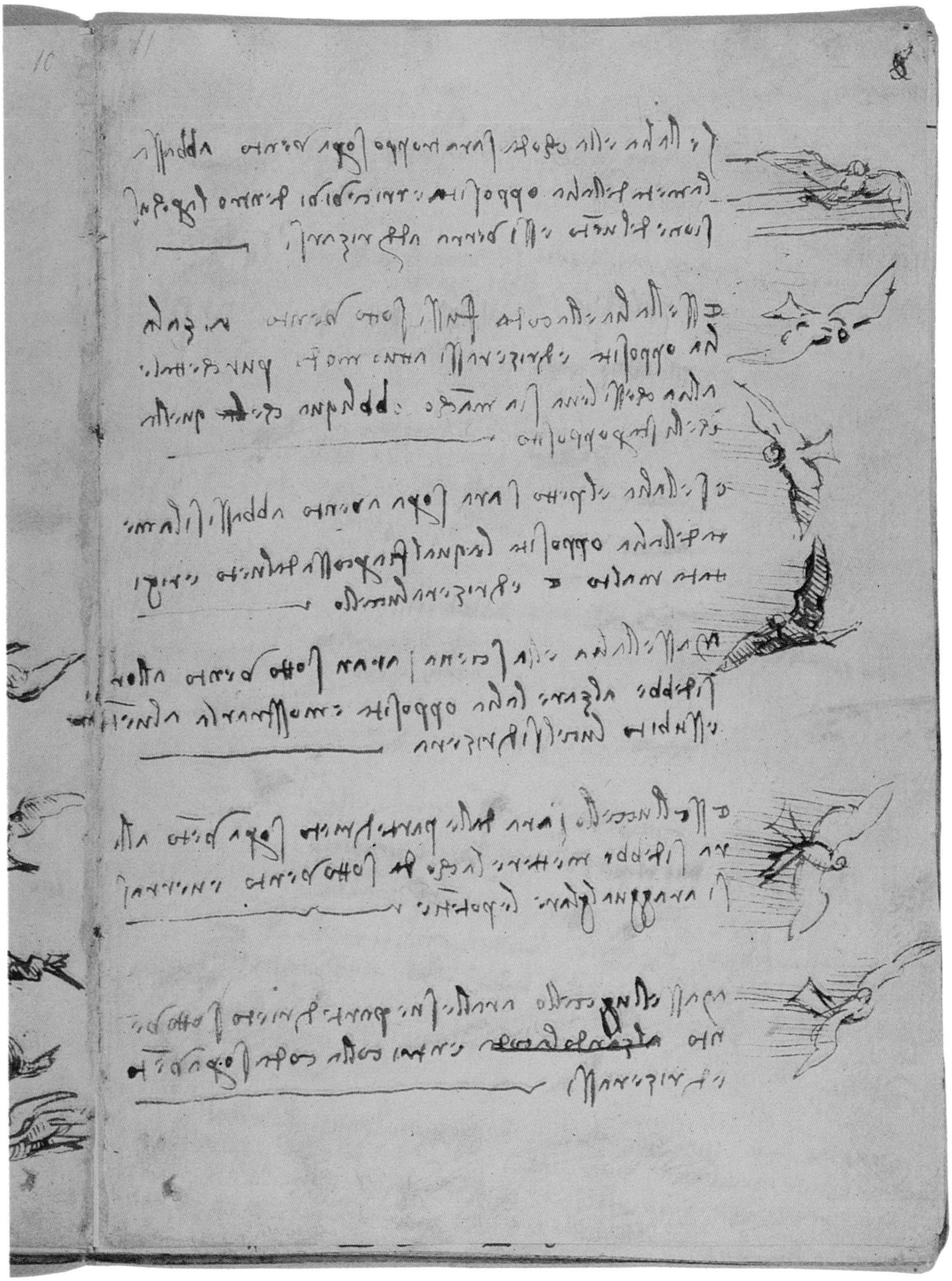

A page from Leonardo da Vinci's *Notebooks*.

SCALA/Art Resource

*The Last Supper.* c. 1495–98. Leonardo da Vinci.

Santa Maria delle Grazie, Milan. Photo: SCALA/Art Resource

Ah, but he painted like an angel. Leonardo's name would live forever just for his painting of *The Last Supper.* It is the most famous religious painting in the history of art. He also painted the *Mona Lisa,* the most famous portrait in the history of art. On these two works alone his reputation as a genius rests. And what of his marvelous *Notebooks*? Nearly forgotten now.

We decided to let our imagination wander. *Why* did Leonardo draw the picture of a sixty-foot crossbow in his notebook? *Why* did he draw the face of a warrior, shouting?

So we made up some stories. We added Rigo Leone as a make-believe friend for Leonardo to talk to. Read on— Leonardo is worth knowing.

"How can you be so calm?" asked Rigo. "Aren't you afraid to die?"

Rigo and Leonardo were lying on the shell-covered beach of a tiny offshore island, bound from head to foot in yards of rope, abandoned and left to die. The moon, full and bright, revealed a cold and rocky landscape.

"We are doomed, Leonardo. Our enemies triumph at last. We shall starve to death or die of thirst, and the crabs and birds will pick our bones white. It is a terrible way to die, Leonardo."

"Why," said Leonardo cheerfully, "you give up life when you give up hope, my friend. I have already thought of *six* ways to escape!"

Rigo shook his head in despair. Poor Leonardo. Clearly, he had lost his senses.

"Lift your head, Rigo, and look up there beyond the beach. You see those trees? Let us therefore use them to make a great bow and arrow! If a six-foot bow will send its shaft three hundred feet, then a sixty-foot bow will send its arrow three *thousand* feet. That will reach the mainland! We will build a simple machine of wood to wind it up, use our ropes for bowstring and winding, and tie a message to the arrow. You understand? It will be quickly seen, easily found, and we will soon be rescued!"

"But it must be nearly half a mile across the water," said Rigo, "and we are tied like chickens for the market."

*157* ✌

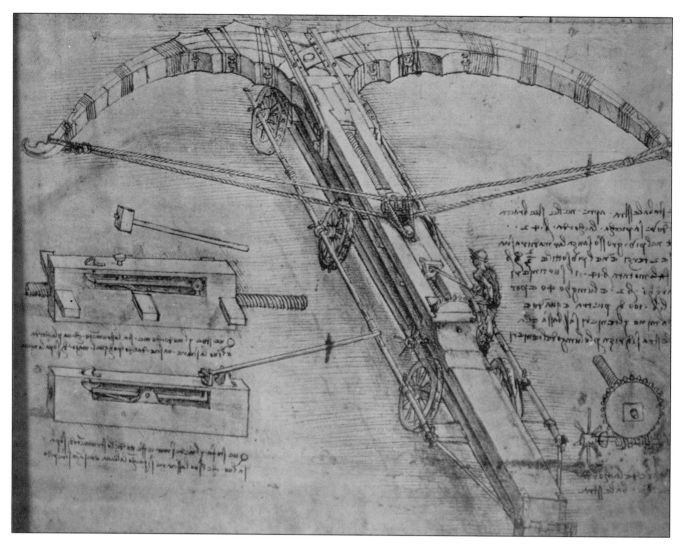

*Giant Crossbow.* Leonardo da Vinci.

Codex Atlanticus, fol. 53r. Biblioteca Ambrosiana, Milan. From Art Resource

Leonardo rolled to his knees and stood, snapping the rope from his chest and arms. "The shells on our beach have edges sharp as any knife, old friend. Here—let me untie your knots."

"You spoke of six ways to escape," said Rigo, rubbing his arms. "Are the other five equally silly?"

"Oh, they are much simpler, I admit. A raft for one. A signal fire by night for two. Or smoke signals by day for three. A kite to fly a message across the water for four. Our great bow and arrow, as I say for—"

"These visions of yours, Leonardo. Will they really work? Or do you tell me stories to ease my mind?"

"They will work, my friend. Anything the mind can reason, the hand can build." Leonardo spoke with quiet sureness.

Rigo's eyes gleamed. "Then let us build the great bow, Leonardo! It will make a splendid sight—the greatest bow and arrow in the history of the world!"

Leonardo smiled. "Of course, there *is* that sixth way to escape."

"I like the thought of the great bow," said Rigo firmly. "Still—what is this sixth way?"

"Why, since the mainland is only half a mile away, all I need do is spend a few minutes teaching you to float."

"Float?" asked Rigo, blankly.

"Since I can swim, I will simply tow you to freedom. Come along, man. Get undressed."

159

"One thing I do not understand, Leonardo," said Rigo.

"And what may that be, my friend?"

"In your notebooks you have surely drawn or written about everything under the sun—even about the bones of the body. God alone can keep count, for I cannot."

"No mystery, Rigo. I want to know everything. My notebooks hold the record of all that I study."

"No man can know everything, not even you!"

"Yet it pleases me to try."

"Hmph. But what I do not understand is this," said Rigo grumpily. "Of all the pictures in your notebook, do you realize that you have never drawn your own face?"

"A self-portrait? Quite right, Rigo. I never have." Leonardo selected a sharpened stick of carbon and gazed into the wall mirror for a long moment. Sketching rapidly, he drew an exact profile of his own face, the mouth open in a great shout.

Rigo nodded his approval. "Yes, that is you, right enough. But why no hair? And why do you shout?"

The artist dusted the carbon from his fingertips. "I need a shouting warrior in my drawing for the Battle of Anghiari. Since he will wear a helmet, no hair will show. Therefore I do not draw it."

"And what does he shout?"

Leonardo grinned. "What do *you* shout in the heat of battle?"

160

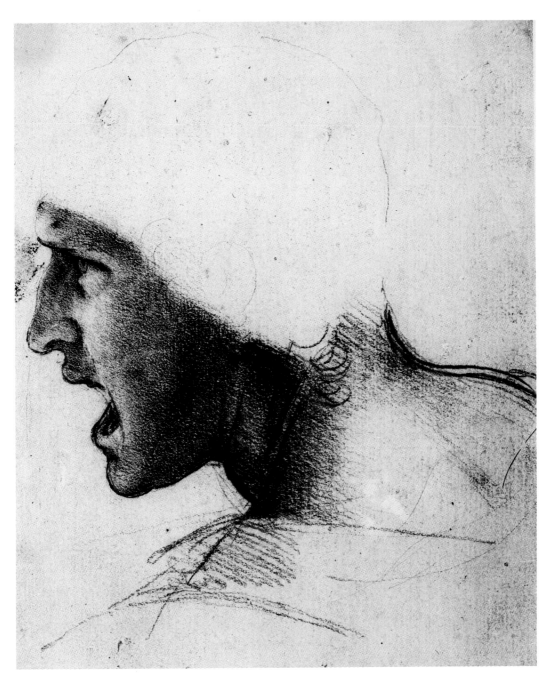

*Warrior Shouting.* Leonardo da Vinci.

Szepmuveszeti Museum, Budapest

Rigo shrugged. "My blood boils and I shout. I cannot remember."

"Just so. When you remember what you shout in battle, you will know what our warrior shouts as well."

# ROXABOXEN

Alice McLerran

*illustrated by Barbara Cooney*

Marian called it Roxaboxen. (She always knew the name of everything.) There across the road, it looked like any rocky hill—nothing but sand and rocks, some old wooden boxes, cactus and greasewood and thorny ocotillo—but it was a special place.

The street between Roxaboxen and the houses curved like a river, so Marian named it the River Rhode. After that you had to ford a river to reach Roxaboxen.

Of course all of Marian's sisters came: Anna May and Frances and little Jean. Charles from next door, even though he was twelve. Oh, and Eleanor, naturally, and Jamie with his brother Paul. Later on there were others, but these were the first.

Well, not really the first. Roxaboxen had always been there and must have belonged to others, long before.

When Marian dug up a tin box filled with round black pebbles everyone knew what it was: it was a buried treasure. Those pebbles were the money of Roxaboxen. You could

still find others like them if you looked hard enough. So some days became treasure-hunting days, with everybody trying to find that special kind. And then on other days you might just find one without even looking.

A town of Roxaboxen began to grow, traced in lines of stone: Main Street first, edged with the whitest ones, and then the houses. Charles made his of the biggest stones.

After all, he was the oldest. At first the houses were very plain, but soon they all began to add more rooms. The old wooden boxes could be shelves or tables or anything you wanted. You could find pieces of pottery for dishes. Round pieces were best.

Later on there was a town hall. Marian was mayor, of course; that was just the way she was. Nobody minded.

After a while they added other streets. Frances moved to one of them and built herself a new house outlined in desert glass, of amber, amethyst, and sea-green: A house of jewels.

And because everybody had plenty of money, there were plenty of shops. Jean helped Anna May in the bakery—pies and cakes and bread baked warm in the sun. There were two ice cream parlors. Was Paul's ice cream the best, or Eleanor's? Everybody kept trying them both. (In Roxaboxen you can eat all the ice cream you want.)

Everybody had a car. All you needed was something round for a steering wheel. Of course, if you broke the speed limit you had to go to jail. The jail had cactus on the floor to make it uncomfortable, and Jamie was the policeman. Anna May, quiet little Anna May, was always speeding— you'd think she liked to go to jail.

But ah, if you had a horse, you could go as fast as the wind. There were no speed limits for horses, and you didn't have to stay on the roads.

All you needed for a horse was a stick and some kind of bridle, and you could gallop anywhere.

Sometimes there were wars. Once there was a great war, boys against girls. Charles and Marian were the generals. The girls had Fort Irene, and they were all girl scouts. The boys made a fort at the other end of Roxaboxen, and they were all bandits.

Oh, the raids were fierce, loud with whooping and the stamping of horses! The whirling swords of ocotillo had sharp thorns—but when you reached your fort you were safe.

Roxaboxen had a cemetery, in case anyone died, but the only grave in it was for a dead lizard. Each year when the cactus bloomed, they decorated the grave with flowers.

Sometimes in the winter, when everybody was at school and the weather was bad, no one went to Roxaboxen at all, not for weeks and weeks. But it didn't matter; Roxaboxen was always waiting. Roxaboxen was always there. And spring came, and the ocotillo blossomed, and everybody sucked the honey from its flowers, and everybody built new rooms, and everybody decided to have jeweled windows. That summer there were three new houses on the east slope and two new shops on Main Street.

And so it went. The seasons changed, and the years went by. Roxaboxen was always there.

The years went by, and the seasons changed, until at last the friends had all grown tall, and one by one, they moved away to other houses, to other towns. So you might think that was the end of Roxaboxen—but oh, no.

Because none of them ever forgot Roxaboxen. Not one of them ever forgot. Years later, Marian's children listened to stories of that place and fell asleep dreaming dreams of Roxaboxen. Gray-haired Charles picked up a black pebble on the beach and stood holding it, remembering Roxaboxen.

More than fifty years later, Frances went back and Roxaboxen was still there. She could see the white stones bordering Main Street, and there where she had built her house the desert glass still glowed—amethyst, amber, and sea-green.

169

### MEET BARBARA COONEY, ILLUSTRATOR

*Artist Barbara Cooney saw Roxaboxen as one of her "toughest assignments yet: constructing a magical world out of something that wasn't there." She made two trips to the desert, where she found*
*"a small tan hill dotted with stones and rocks, a scattering of desert plants, and now lots of broken glass and an old car chassis." But accompanied by Alice McLerran's eighty-year-old Aunt Frances (former Roxaboxenite), Cooney felt the magic and spirit of Roxaboxen begin to emerge—a magic found in the minds and hearts of the children who played there.*

# IT COULD ALWAYS BE WORSE

retold and illustrated
by Margot Zemach

Once upon a time in a small village a poor unfortunate man lived with his mother, his wife, and his six children in a little one-room hut. Because they were so crowded, the man and his wife often argued. The children were noisy, and they fought. In winter, when the nights were long and the days were cold, life was especially hard. The hut was full of crying and quarreling. One day, when the poor unfortunate man couldn't stand it any more, he ran to the Rabbi for advice.

"Holy Rabbi," he cried, "things are in a bad way with me, and getting worse. We are so poor that my mother, my wife, my six children, and I all live together in one small hut. We are too crowded, and there's so much noise. Help me, Rabbi. I'll do whatever you say."

The Rabbi thought and pulled on his beard. At last he said, "Tell me, my poor man, do you have any animals, perhaps a chicken or two?"

"Yes," said the man. "I do have a few chickens, also a rooster and a goose."

"Ah, fine," said the Rabbi. "Now go home and take the chickens, the rooster, and the goose into your hut to live with you."

"Yes indeed, Rabbi," said the man, though he was a bit surprised.

The poor unfortunate man hurried home and took the chickens, the rooster, and the goose out of the shed and into his little hut.

When some days or a week had gone by, life in the hut was worse than before. Now with the quarreling and crying there was honking, crowing, and clucking. There were

feathers in the soup. The hut stayed just as small and the children grew bigger. When the poor unfortunate man couldn't stand it any longer, he again ran to the Rabbi for help.

"Holy Rabbi," he cried, "see what a misfortune has befallen me. Now with the crying and quarreling, with the honking, clucking, and crowing, there are feathers in the soup. Rabbi, it couldn't be worse. Help me, please."

The Rabbi listened and thought. At last he said, "Tell me, do you happen to have a goat?"

"Oh, yes, I do have an old goat, but he's not worth much."

"Excellent," said the Rabbi. "Now go home and take the old goat into your hut to live with you."

"Ah, no! Do you really mean it, Rabbi?" cried the man.

"Come, come now, my good man, and do as I say at once," said the Rabbi.

The poor unfortunate man tramped back home with his head hanging down and took the old goat into his hut.

When some days or a week had gone by, life in the little hut was much worse. Now, with the crying, quarreling, clucking, honking, and crowing, the goat went wild, pushing and butting everyone with his horns. The hut seemed smaller, the children grew bigger.

When the poor unfortunate man couldn't stand it another minute, he again ran to the Rabbi.

"Holy Rabbi, help me!" he screamed. "Now the goat is running wild. My life is a nightmare."

The Rabbi listened and thought. At last he said, "Tell me, my poor man. Is it possible that you have a cow? Young or old doesn't matter."

"Yes, Rabbi, it's true I have a cow," said the poor man fearfully.

"Go home then," said the Rabbi, "and take the cow into your hut."

"Oh, no, surely not, Rabbi!" cried the man.

"Do it at once," said the Rabbi.

The poor unfortunate man trudged home with a heavy heart and took the cow into his hut. Is the Rabbi crazy? he thought.

When some days or a week had gone by, life in the hut was very much worse than before. Everyone quarreled, even the chickens. The goat ran wild. The cow trampled everything. The poor man could hardly believe his misfortune. At last, when he could stand it no longer, he ran to the Rabbi for help.

"Holy Rabbi," he shrieked, "help me, save me, the end of the world has come! The cow is trampling everything. There is no room even to breathe. It's worse than a nightmare!"

The Rabbi listened and thought. At last he said, "Go home now, my poor unfortunate man, and let the animals out of your hut."

"I will, I will, I'll do it right away," said the man.

The poor unfortunate man hurried home and let the cow, the goat, the chickens, the goose, and the rooster out of his little hut.

That night the poor man and all his family slept peacefully. There was no crowing, no clucking, no honking. There was plenty of room to breathe.

The very next day the poor man ran back to the Rabbi.

"Holy Rabbi," he cried, "you have made life sweet for me. With just my family in the hut, it's so quiet, so roomy, so peaceful . . . What a pleasure!"

MEET MARGOT ZEMACH,
AUTHOR AND ILLUSTRATOR

*"Children need detail, color, excellence— the best a person can do. I always think, when I'm drawing the view of a town or the inside of a hut: 'Would I have liked to live there?'. . . to a certain extent, one can invent one's own styles of dress and house shapes. But things have to be made real. The food has to be what you'd want to eat, the bed has to be what you'd want to get into right away. But, all in all, I'm not sure that one should consciously bear in mind that the drawings are meant for the gaze of children. If I make a book for children, I draw it the same as I'd draw for grownups."*

# THE BREMEN TOWN MUSICIANS

## The Brothers Grimm
### *illustrated by Josef Paleček*

A man once had a donkey who had worked patiently for many long years carrying sacks to the mill, but now his strength was failing and he was less and less useful.

So his master decided to get rid of him, but the donkey, realizing that something was wrong, ran away and set off for the town of Bremen. "I can always join the Bremen Town Band," he thought.

When he had been walking along for a while, he met a hound lying by the roadside, panting as if he had run and run until he was worn out.

"Why are you panting like that, Biter?" asked the donkey.

"Because I'm old," said the dog, "and I'm getting weaker every day. I can't go hunting anymore either. My master was going to kill me, and I ran away. But how am I to earn a living now?"

"I tell you what," said the donkey. "I'm going to Bremen. I'm going to join the Bremen Town Band. Why don't you come with me, and you can join it too. I'll play the lute, and you can beat the drums."

The dog thought that was a good idea, so they went on together.

Before long they met a cat, sitting by the roadside and looking as miserable as three days of wet weather.

"Well, what's the matter with you, Whiskers, old fellow?" asked the donkey.

"It's no joke when people are out for your blood, let me tell you!" said the cat. "I'm getting old now, my teeth aren't so sharp, and I'd rather sit by the fire and sleep than chase mice, so my mistress was going to drown me. I got away just in time, but now I don't know what to do. Where am I to go?"

"Come to Bremen with us! You're used to singing serenades, so you can be a musician too."

The cat thought that was a good idea, and he went along with them.

Then the three fugitives passed a farmyard. There was the farm rooster, sitting on the gate, crowing for all he was worth.

"Your crowing goes right through me," said the donkey. "What's up?"

"I was forecasting fine weather," said the rooster, "because it's a holiday. But there are people coming to dinner on Sunday, which is tomorrow, and the farmer's wife has told the cook she wants me in the soup. They're going to cut my head off this evening. So I'm crowing and crowing while I still can!"

"I tell you what, Redcomb," said the donkey," why not come with us instead? We're going to Bremen. You'll find anywhere's better than being dead. You have a good voice, and if we make music together, it will be a fine noise!"

The rooster liked the donkey's suggestion, and all four of them went along together.

However, they couldn't reach the town of Bremen in one day, and that evening they came to a forest and decided to spend the night there.

The donkey and the dog lay down under a big tree, the cat climbed into its branches, and the rooster flew to the very top, where he would be safest. Before going to sleep, though, he looked north, south, east, and west, and he thought he saw a little spark burning in the distance. So he called down to his companions to tell them there must be a house not far off, because he could see a light shining.

"Then we'd better get up and go there," said the donkey. "It's not very comfortable here!"

And the dog agreed. A bone or so and a bit of meat, he said, would suit him nicely.

So they set off for the place where the light was. Soon they saw it shining brighter, and it grew larger and larger, and at last they came to a robbers' house, brightly lit.

The donkey, being the biggest, went up to the window and looked in.

"What can you see, Greycoat?" asked the dog.

"What can I see?" replied the donkey. "I can see a table covered with good things to eat and drink, and robbers sitting at it making merry."

"We could certainly make good use of those things to eat and drink," said the rooster.

"Hee haw, I wish we were sitting there!" said the donkey.

Wondering how to chase the robbers out of the house, the animals talked it over, and at last they thought of a way.

The donkey put his forefeet up on the windowsill, the dog climbed on the donkey's back, the cat climbed on the dog's back, and finally the rooster flew up and settled on the cat's head.

When they were ready, a signal was given, and they all began making music together: the donkey brayed,

the dog barked,

the cat mewed,

and the rooster crowed.

Then they crashed through the window and into the room, to the sound of breaking glass.

The robbers jumped up when they heard that frightful noise, thinking a ghost was coming in, and they ran out into the forest in terror.

So then the four companions sat down at the table, set to work on the food that was left, and they ate as if they weren't going to eat again for a month. When the four musicians had finished, they put out the light and looked for a place to sleep, each according to his nature and his notions of comfort. The donkey lay down on the dungheap, the dog lay down behind the door, the cat lay in the warm ashes on the hearth, and the rooster settled on the beam at the top of the ceiling. Since they were tired from their long journey, they soon fell asleep.

When it was past midnight, and the robbers, lurking in the distance, saw that there was no light in the house anymore, and all seemed quiet, the robber chief said,

"We shouldn't have let ourselves be scared like that!" And he told one of his men to go and take a look at the house.

The robber found the house perfectly quiet. He went into the kitchen to get a light, and thinking that the cat's glowing, fiery eyes were live coals, he touched a candle to them, thinking it would catch fire. But the cat was not

amused, and leaped for his face, hissing and scratching. The terrified robber ran for it, and tried to get out of the back door. However, the dog was lying there, and jumped up and bit his leg. And as he ran across the yard and past the dungheap the donkey gave him a good kick with his hind leg.

As for the rooster, roused from his sleep by all this noise and wide awake now, he sat on his beam and crowed, "Cock-a-doodle-do!"

Then the robber ran for his life, back to the robber chief, and told him, "Oh, there's a terrible old witch in our house. She spat at me and scratched my face with her long fingers. And there's a man behind the door with a knife, and he stabbed me in the leg. And there's a monster in the yard who hit me with a wooden club. And the judge himself is sitting up in the rafters, and he called, 'Cut the rogue in two!' So I ran for it!"

The robbers never dared go back to their house again. But the four Bremen Town Musicians liked it there so much that they never wanted to leave.

In fact, they liked it better every day, and they all lived happily together in their house for a long, long time.

# TWO BIG BEARS

from LITTLE HOUSE IN THE BIG WOODS
by Laura Ingalls Wilder
*illustrated by Garth Williams*

One day Pa said that spring was coming.

In the Big Woods the snow was beginning to thaw. Bits of it dropped from the branches of the trees and made little holes in the softening snowbanks below. At noon all the big icicles along the eaves of the little house quivered and sparkled in the sunshine, and drops of water hung trembling at their tips.

Pa said he must go to town to trade the furs of the wild animals he had been trapping all winter. So one evening he made a big bundle of them. There were so many furs that when they were packed tightly and tied together they made a bundle almost as big as Pa.

Very early one morning Pa strapped the bundle of furs on his shoulders, and started to walk to town. There were so many furs to carry that he could not take his gun.

Ma was worried, but Pa said that by starting before sun-up and walking very fast all day he could get home again before dark.

The nearest town was far away. Laura and Mary had never seen a town. They had never seen a store. They had never seen even two houses standing together. But they knew that in a town there were many houses, and a store full of candy and calico and other wonderful things— powder, and shot, and salt, and store sugar.

They knew that Pa would trade his furs to the store-keeper for beautiful things from town, and all day they were expecting the presents he would bring them. When the sun sank low above the treetops and no more drops fell from the tips of the icicles they began to watch eagerly for Pa.

The sun sank out of sight, the woods grew dark, and he did not come. Ma started supper and set the table, but he did not come. It was time to do the chores, and still he had not come.

Ma said that Laura might come with her while she milked the cow. Laura could carry the lantern.

So Laura put on her coat and Ma buttoned it up. And Laura put her hands into her red mittens that hung by a red yarn string around her neck, while Ma lighted the candle in the lantern.

Laura was proud to be helping Ma with the milking, and she carried the lantern very carefully. Its sides were of tin, with places cut in them for the candle-light to shine through.

When Laura walked behind Ma on the path to the barn, the little bits of candle-light from the lantern leaped all around her on the snow. The night was not yet quite dark. The woods were dark, but there was a gray light on the snowy path, and in the sky there were a few faint stars. The stars did not look as warm and bright as the little lights that came from the lantern.

Laura was surprised to see the dark shape of Sukey, the brown cow, standing at the barnyard gate. Ma was surprised, too.

It was too early in the spring for Sukey to be let out in the Big Woods to eat grass. She lived in the barn. But sometimes on warm days Pa left the door of her stall open so she could come into the barnyard. Now Ma and Laura saw her behind the bars, waiting for them.

Ma went up to the gate, and pushed against it to open it. But it did not open very far, because there was Sukey, standing against it. Ma said, "Sukey, get over!" She reached across the gate and slapped Sukey's shoulder.

Just then one of the dancing little bits of light from the lantern jumped between the bars of the gate, and Laura saw long, shaggy, black fur, and two little, glittering eyes.

Sukey had thin, short, brown fur. Sukey had large, gentle eyes.

Ma said, "Laura, walk back to the house."

So Laura turned around and began to walk toward the house. Ma came behind her. When they had gone part way, Ma snatched her up, lantern and all, and ran. Ma ran with her into the house, and slammed the door.

Then Laura said, "Ma, was it a bear?"

"Yes, Laura," Ma said. "It was a bear."

Laura began to cry. She hung on to Ma and sobbed, "Oh, will he eat Sukey?"

"No," Ma said, hugging her. "Sukey is safe in the barn. Think, Laura—all those big, heavy logs in the barn walls. And the door is heavy and solid, made to keep bears out. No, the bear cannot get in and eat Sukey."

Laura felt better then. "But he could have hurt us, couldn't he?" she asked.

"He didn't hurt us," Ma said. "You were a good girl, Laura, to do exactly as I told you, and to do it quickly, without asking why."

Ma was trembling, and she began to laugh a little. "To think," she said, "I've slapped a bear!"

Then she put supper on the table for Laura and Mary. Pa had not come yet. He didn't come. Laura and Mary were undressed, and they said their prayers and snuggled into the trundle bed.

Ma sat by the lamp, mending one of Pa's shirts. The house seemed cold and still and strange, without Pa.

Laura listened to the wind in the Big Woods. All around the house the wind went crying as though it were lost in the dark and the cold. The wind sounded frightened.

Ma finished mending the shirt. Laura saw her fold it slowly and carefully. She smoothed it with her hand. Then she did a thing she had never done before. She went to the door and pulled the leather latch-string through its hole in the door, so that nobody could get in from outside unless she lifted the latch. She came and took Carrie, all limp and sleeping, out of the big bed.

She saw that Laura and Mary were still awake, and she said to them: "Go to sleep, girls. Everything is all right. Pa will be here in the morning."

Then she went back to her rocking chair and sat there rocking gently and holding Baby Carrie in her arms.

She was sitting up late, waiting for Pa, and Laura and Mary meant to stay awake, too, till he came. But at last they went to sleep.

In the morning Pa was there. He had brought candy for Laura and Mary, and two pieces of pretty calico to make them each a dress. Mary's was a china-blue pattern on a white ground, and Laura's was dark red with little golden-brown dots on it. Ma had calico for a dress, too; it was brown, with a big, feathery white pattern all over it.

They were all happy because Pa had got such good prices for his furs that he could afford to get them such beautiful presents.

The tracks of the big bear were all around the barn, and there were marks of his claws on the walls. But Sukey and the horses were safe inside.

All that day the sun shone, the snow melted, and little streams of water ran from the icicles, which all the time grew thinner. Before the sun set that night, the bear tracks were only shapeless marks in the wet, soft snow.

After supper Pa took Laura and Mary on his knees and said he had a new story to tell them.

"When I went to town yesterday with the furs I found it hard walking in the soft snow. It took me a long time to get to town, and other men with furs had come in earlier to do their trading. The storekeeper was busy, and I had to wait until he could look at my furs.

"Then we had to bargain about the price of each one, and then I had to pick out the things I wanted to take in trade.

"So it was nearly sundown before I could start home.

"I tried to hurry, but the walking was hard and I was tired, so I had not gone far before night came. And I was alone in the Big Woods without my gun.

"There were still six miles to walk, and I came along as fast as I could. The night grew darker and darker, and I wished for my gun, because I knew that some of the bears had come out of their winter dens. I had seen their tracks when I went to town in the morning.

"Bears are hungry and cross at this time of year; you know they have been sleeping in their dens all winter long with nothing to eat, and that makes them thin and angry when they wake up. I did not want to meet one.

"I hurried along as quick as I could in the dark. By and by the stars gave a little light. It was still black as pitch where the woods were thick, but in the open places I could see, dimly. I could see the snowy road ahead a little way, and I could see the dark woods standing all around me. I was glad when I came into an open place where the stars gave me this faint light.

"All the time I was watching, as well as I could, for bears. I was listening for the sounds they make when they go carelessly through the bushes.

"Then I came again into an open place, and there, right in the middle of my road, I saw a big black bear.

"He was standing up on his hind legs, looking at me. I could see his eyes shine. I could see his pig-snout. I could even see one of his claws, in the starlight.

"My scalp prickled, and my hair stood straight up. I stopped in my tracks, and stood still. The bear did not move. There he stood, looking at me.

"I knew it would do no good to try to go around him. He would follow me into the dark woods, where he could see better than I could. I did not want to fight a winter-starved bear in the dark. Oh, how I wished for my gun!

"I had to pass that bear, to get home. I thought that if I could scare him, he might get out of the road and let me go by. So I took a deep breath, and suddenly I shouted with all my might and ran at him, waving my arms.

"He didn't move.

"I did not run very far toward him, I tell you! I stopped and looked at him, and he stood looking at me. Then I shouted again. There he stood. I kept on shouting and waving my arms, but he did not budge.

"Well, it would do me no good to run away. There were other bears in the woods. I might meet one any time. I might as well deal with this one as with another. Besides, I was coming home to Ma and you girls. I would never get here, if I ran away from everything in the woods that scared me.

"So at last I looked around, and I got a good big club, a solid, heavy branch that had been broken from a tree by the weight of snow in the winter.

"I lifted it up in my hands, and I ran straight at that bear. I swung my club as hard as I could and brought it down, bang! on his head.

"And there he still stood, for he was nothing but a big, black, burned stump!

"I had passed it on my way to town that morning. It wasn't a bear at all. I only thought it was a bear, because I had been thinking all the time about bears and being afraid I'd meet one."

"It really wasn't a bear at all?" Mary asked.

"No, Mary, it wasn't a bear at all. There I had been yelling, and dancing, and waving my arms, all by myself in the Big Woods, trying to scare a stump!"

Laura said: "Ours was really a bear. But we were not scared, because we thought it was Sukey."

Pa did not say anything, but he hugged her tighter.

"Oo-oo! That bear might have eaten Ma and me all up!" Laura said, snuggling closer to him. "But Ma walked right up to him and slapped him, and he didn't do anything at all. Why didn't he do anything?"

"I guess he was too surprised to do anything, Laura," Pa said. "I guess he was afraid, when the lantern shone in his eyes. And when Ma walked up to him and slapped him, he knew *she* wasn't afraid."

"Well, you were brave, too," Laura said. "Even if it was only a stump, you thought it was a bear. You'd have hit him on the head with a club, if he *had* been a bear, wouldn't you, Pa?"

"Yes," said Pa, "I would. You see, I had to."

Then Ma said it was bedtime. She helped Laura and Mary undress and button up their red flannel nightgowns. They knelt down by the trundle bed and said their prayers.

## MEET LAURA INGALLS WILDER, AUTHOR

Little House in the Big Woods *was first published in 1932, with great success. Of the book, Laura Ingalls Wilder has said:*

*"These were family stories and I believed they should be preserved. When to my surprise the book made such a success and children all over the U.S. wrote to me begging for more stories, I began to think what a wonderful childhood I had had. How I had seen the whole frontier, the woods, the Indian country of the great plains, the frontier towns, the building of railroads in wild, unsettled country, homesteading and farmers coming in to take possession. I realized that I had seen and lived it all. . . . I wanted children now to understand more about the beginning of things, to know what is behind the things they see—what it is that made America as they know it. . . . Every story . . . all the circumstances, each incident are true."*

## MEET GARTH WILLIAMS, ILLUSTRATOR

*When Garth Williams was first asked to illustrate the new edition of the* Little House *books, he was very excited. But he knew very little of the West and wanted to see the country that formed the background for the stories. So he went to visit Mr. and Mrs. Wilder in Mansfield, Missouri, where they were living. Then he followed the route that the Ingalls family had taken in their covered wagon. He gathered a great deal of information to use in his illustrations. He says, "Illustrating books is not just making pictures of the houses, the people and the articles mentioned by the author; the artist has to see everything with the same eyes. For example, an architect would have described the sod house on the bank of Plum Creek as extremely primitive, unhealthy and undesirable—nothing to seal the walls from dampness, no ventilation, no light. But to Laura's fresh young eyes it was a pleasant house, surrounded by flowers and with the music of a running stream and rustling leaves."*

195

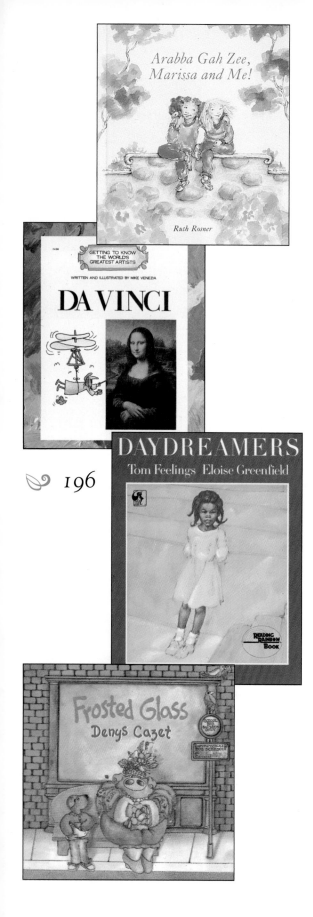

*Arabba Gah Zee, Marissa and Me!* by Ruth Rosner. Two friends with incredible imaginations love to play at being everything from spies to rock stars.

*Da Vinci* by Mike Venezia. This book is by the same author as *Picasso*. You will have fun learning about the life of Leonardo da Vinci and looking at some of his paintings and drawings.

*Daydreamers* by Eloise Greenfield. You'll enjoy this delightful poem that describes the world of daydreamers.

*Frosted Glass* by Denys Cazet. Gregory's imagination sometimes gets him into trouble, but what wonderful works of art he produces!

*Walter's Magic Wand* by Eric Houghton. With his imagination and a magic wand he made, Walter makes exciting things happen in the library.

*Jenny Archer, Author* by Ellen Conford. Although she likes to write, Jenny Archer is stumped by an assignment to write her autobiography until she uses her imagination to spice up her life story.

*My Father Doesn't Know About the Woods and Me* by Dennis Haseley. As a young boy walks in the woods with his father, he wonders whether his father knows his secret.

*The Value of Imagination: The Story of Charles Dickens* by Spencer Johnson. This biography of the English novelist Charles Dickens stresses the value of an imaginative mind.

197

198

# MONEY

199

# A NEW COAT FOR ANNA

Harriet Ziefert

*illustrated by* Anita Lobel

Winter had come and Anna needed a new coat. The fuzzy blue coat that she had worn for so many winters was no longer fuzzy and it was very small.

Last winter Anna's mother had said, "When the war is over, we will be able to buy things again and I will get you a nice new coat."

But when the war ended the stores remained empty. There still were no coats. There was hardly any food. And no one had any money.

Anna's mother wondered how she could get Anna a new coat. Then she had an idea. "Anna, I have no money," she said, "but I still have Grandfather's gold watch and some other nice things. Maybe we can use them to get what we need for a new coat. First we need wool. Tomorrow we will visit a farmer and see about getting some."

The next day Anna and her mother walked to a nearby farm.

"Anna needs a new coat," Anna's mother told the farmer. "I have no money, but I will give you this fine gold watch if you will give me enough wool from your sheep to make a coat."

The farmer said, "What a good idea! But you will have to wait until spring when I shear my sheep's winter wool. Then I can trade you their wool for your gold watch."

Anna waited for spring to come. Almost every Sunday she and her mother visited the sheep. She would always ask them, "Is your wool growing?" The sheep would always answer, "Baaa!" Then she would feed them nice fresh hay and give them hugs.

At Christmastime Anna brought them paper necklaces and apples and sang carols.

When spring came the farmer sheared the sheep's wool.

"Does it hurt them?" asked Anna.

"No, Anna," said the farmer. "It is just like getting a haircut."

When he had enough wool to make a coat, the farmer showed Anna how to card the wool. "It's like untangling the knots in your hair," he told Anna.

Then he gave Anna's mother a big bag of wool and Anna's mother gave him the gold watch.

Anna and her mother took the bag of wool to an old woman who had a spinning wheel.

"Anna needs a new coat," Anna's mother told the woman. "I have no money, but I will give you this beautiful lamp if you will spin this wool into yarn."

The woman said, "A lamp. That's just what I need. But I cannot spin quickly, for I am old and my fingers are stiff. Come back when the cherries are ripe and I will have your yarn."

When summer came, Anna and her mother returned. Anna's mother gave the old woman the lamp and the old woman gave them the yarn—and a basket of delicious red cherries.

"Anna, what color coat would you like?" Anna's mother asked.

"A red one!" Anna answered.

"Then we will pick some lingonberries," said Anna's mother. "They make a beautiful red dye."

At the end of the summer, Anna's mother knew just the place in the woods to find the ripest lingonberries.

Anna and her mother boiled water in a big pot and put the berries into it. The water turned a deep red. Anna's mother dipped the pale yarn into it.

Soon red yarn was hanging up to dry on a clothesline strung across the kitchen.

When it dried, Anna and her mother wound the yarn into balls.

They took the yarn to the weaver.

"Anna needs a new coat," Anna's mother said. "I have no money, but I will give you this garnet necklace if you will weave this yarn into cloth."

The weaver said, "What a pretty necklace. I will be happy to weave your yarn. Come back in two weeks."

When Anna and her mother returned, the weaver gave them a bolt of beautiful red cloth. Anna's mother gave the weaver the sparkling garnet necklace.

The next day Anna and her mother set off to see the tailor.

"Winter is coming and Anna needs a new coat," Anna's mother told the tailor. "I have no money, but I will give you this porcelain teapot if you will make a coat from this cloth."

The tailor said, "That's a pretty teapot. Anna, I'd be very happy to make you a new coat, but first I must take your measurements."

He measured her shoulders. He measured her arms. He measured from the back of her neck to the back of her knees. Then he said, "Come back next week and I will have your coat."

The tailor set to work making a pattern, cutting the cloth, pinning, and sewing and stitching and snipping. He worked and worked for almost a whole week. When he was finished, he found six pretty matching buttons in his button box and sewed them on the coat.

He hung the coat proudly in the window for everyone to see.

205

When Anna and her mother returned to the tailor's shop, Anna tried on her new coat. She twirled around in front of the mirror. The coat was perfect!

Anna thanked the tailor. Anna's mother thanked him, too, and gave him the pretty porcelain teapot.

Anna wore her new coat home. She stopped at every store to look at her reflection in the window.

When they got home her mother said, "Christmas will soon be here, and I think this year we could have a little celebration."

Anna said, "Oh, yes, and please could we invite all the people who helped to make my coat?"

"Yes," said Anna's mother. "And I will make a Christmas cake just like I used to."

Anna gave her mother a big hug.

On Christmas Eve the farmer, the spinner, the weaver, and the tailor came to Anna's house. They all thought Anna looked beautiful in her new coat.

The Christmas cake that Anna's mother baked was
delicious. Everyone agreed that this was the best Christmas
they had had in a long time.

On Christmas Day Anna visited
the sheep. "Thank you for the
wool, sheep," she said. "Do you like
my pretty new coat?"

The sheep seemed to smile as
they answered, "Baaa! Baaa!"

# MONEY MONEY MONEY

## Ruth Belov Gross
### *illustrated by Leslie Jacobs*

A long time ago there was no money at all in the world. People didn't need money. They got everything they needed by trading things.

The people who lived in Egypt many thousands of years ago traded things. They traded some of the things they didn't need for other things they did need.

Thank you. Here is some beautiful cloth.

I have some extra corn. Could you use it?

Will you give me that jar of honey if I give you some figs?

Yes, I'll trade with you. Take the honey— but give me *all* your figs.

The people who lived in Greece many thousands of years ago traded things too. All over the world, people traded with each other. There is a special name for this kind of trading. The name is *barter*.

209 🌸

I have just made a fine pair of sandals. Will you give me some arrowheads for these sandals?

We don't want any sandals. But if you have some bananas, we'll trade with you.

Most of the time, barter was a good way of getting things. There was one trouble with barter, though. What happened when you had something to trade but nobody wanted it?

Sorry.

I don't have any bananas.

If nobody wanted the things you had, you were out of luck! But—

—what if you had something that almost everybody wanted? Then it was easy to make a trade.

In some places, a long time ago, you could always make a trade if you had a cow. In other places, a long time ago, you could always make a trade if you had pigs or goats or sheep. In all these places, the people used their animals the way we use money. So you can say that cows and pigs and goats and sheep were an early kind of money.

If I give you this nice fat cow, will you give me those knives?

I don't need a cow. But I'll take it anyhow and give you the knives.

Hmmm. I wonder why he'll take my cow. He said he doesn't need a cow . . .

The people around here are always looking for nice fat cows. I'm sure I can trade this cow for something I want . . .

Here is the cow.

Here are the knives.

Animals weren't the only things people used for money, a long time ago. In some places, people used salt for money. Everybody wanted salt for their food. In Rome, the soldiers were even paid in salt!

In some places, people used corn and grain for money.

In some places, people used little shells for money. They were called cowrie shells. You could put them on a string and wear them around your neck. They were supposed to be lucky.

In some places, people used spades and shovels and knives for money. People needed these tools for their crops and animals.

But there was one trouble with the things people used for money.

What if the cows or pigs or goats or sheep got sick?

What if the salt got wet—and washed away?

What if the corn or grain got spoiled?

What if the cowrie shells got smashed?

What if the tools got broken?

Then what could people use for money?

My money doesn't feel well.

After a while, people found better things to use for money. They began to use pieces of metal—

copper and
bronze and
iron and
gold and
silver.

A piece of metal wouldn't get sick.

A piece of metal wouldn't wash away in the rain.

A piece of metal wouldn't get spoiled.

A piece of metal wouldn't get smashed.

A piece of metal wouldn't get broken.

And you could carry your metal money around with you.

You could make pots and tools and other useful things out of metal. You could make beautiful necklaces and rings and bracelets too.

When people began to use metal for money, they used all sizes and shapes of metal. They used lumps of metal, and chunks of metal, and bars of metal. How much could you buy if you had a chunk of copper? The heavier your chunk of copper was, the more you could buy with it.

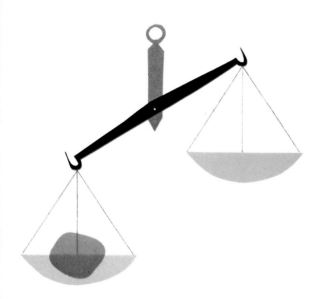

But how did you know how heavy it was? You had to weigh it. When somebody gave you a piece of metal, you weighed it. When you gave somebody else a piece of metal, *he* weighed it. That way, nobody cheated anybody. The metal was weighed every time a person gave another person some

copper or

bronze or

iron or

gold or

silver.

Weighing the metal was a lot of trouble for everybody. Just think what it would be like if the man in the grocery store had to weigh your money every time he sold you some cookies!

At last some men had a good idea. This is what they decided to do: A man would weigh a piece of metal once. He would put a mark on it to show how much it weighed. After that, the metal would not have to be weighed again. The piece of metal was now a *coin*. Everybody could look at it and see how much it was worth.

One day, almost three thousand years ago, the king of a country called Lydia made a new law. The king said that the people of Lydia were not allowed to weigh their own metal and mark it any more. The king's men were the only ones who had the right to make metal into coins.

The king's money was the first real money people had. We say it was the first real money because it was made by the government, just like our money is today.

In Lydia it was against the law to make your own money. Any man who tried would get into trouble.

The king of Lydia made his coins out of gold and silver. The coins looked like lumpy buttons.

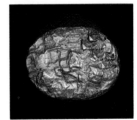

Soon the governments of other countries were making coins too.

Coins made in Greece a long time ago looked something like our pennies and nickels and dimes, only they were thicker and not quite round.

Some of the coins made in Rome did not look like our coins at all. This coin was bigger than a slice of bread. It weighed more than a pound.

Before long, many more countries had their own metal coins.

Let's stop now to see what we know about money. This is what we know:

In the very beginning, before there was any money at all, people just traded with each other.

Later on, animals were money. Salt was money. Corn and grain and shells and tools were money too.

After a while, pieces of metal were money. And then people began to make their pieces of metal into coins.

The first real money was made by the government of a country called Lydia.

Other governments made money for their people after that. People feel safer when the government is in charge of making the money they use.

These things did not happen in a day. They took a long time to happen. And they happened at different times in different places.

People in some parts of the world were still using cows for money when people in other parts of the world were using metal coins.

About three hundred and fifty years ago, some people from England came to live in America. They came to settle in colonies.

When they lived in England, they used metal coins. But when they came to settle in America they did not bring many coins with them. And the king of England wouldn't let anyone make coins in the American colonies. So the settlers didn't have much money. But they found ways to get the things they needed.

What do you think they did?

They traded with each other. They used corn for money, and they used cows for money. They used beaver skins for money, and they used tobacco for money. They used fish and peas and wheat for money, and they used nails and bullets for money. They even used these things to pay their bills and to pay their taxes. People almost always tried to pay their taxes with the skinniest cows they had.

I've come to pay my taxes. Here's my cow.

Do you call that a cow?

TAX COLLECTOR

In many of the American colonies the settlers used little beads made from shells. The shell beads were called *wampum*. Wampum was what the Indians used for money. Six white beads were worth about a penny. Black beads were worth twice as much as white beads. If you had

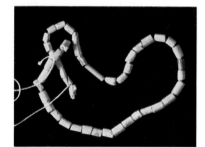

wampum, you could buy beaver skins from the Indians. You could also buy things from other settlers.

The Indians made wampum out of clam shells and periwinkle shells. They strung the wampum beads on thin strips of deer hide. The Indians made beautiful belts and bracelets out of wampum too.

The settlers used French coins and Dutch coins and English coins and Spanish coins. They got some of the coins by selling fish and flour and lumber and furs to other countries. And they got some of the coins from pirates. The pirates came to buy food for themselves and tar and pitch and turpentine for their ships. They paid the settlers with the gold and silver coins they took from other ships at sea.

Again and again the settlers asked the king of England to let them make their own money. Every time they asked, the king said no. He said it was against the law for the settlers in the colonies to make their own money.

The settlers did not like the king's law about money. They did not like some other laws the king made for them. They decided they did not want the king of England to make any of their laws. They wanted to make their own laws.

So the colonies had a war with England. It was called the American Revolution. The colonies won the war. That was about two hundred years ago.

After the American Revolution, the colonies did not belong to England any more. They were not colonies

now. They were *states*. They were the United States of
America. Now they could make their own laws.

Soon the people in the United States had their own
coins. The coins were made by the new government.

This is what two of the coins looked like:

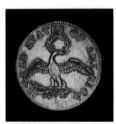

An eagle—$10
This coin was made of gold.

The Smithsonian Institution,
National Museum of American History,
National Numismatic Collection

A half cent
A half cent was made of copper.

American Numismatic Society

The United States government made the coins, but for
a long time it let the banks make the paper money. Now

the government makes all of our money—all of our coins and all of our paper money. If anybody else tries to make coins or paper money, he gets into trouble!

The United States was not the first country to use paper money. People in China used paper money long before any settlers came to America. China was ruled by an emperor, and only the emperor's men could make the paper money. If anybody else tried to make paper money he was in trouble.

Money. Money. Money. It comes in very handy. Children use money to buy ice cream cones. They use it to buy birthday presents for their friends. Sometimes they use it to buy lunch at school.

Grownups use coins and paper money too. But they also use *checks*.

And they use *credit cards*.

Checks and credit cards are things that people can use instead of the money the government makes. A check is like a little letter to the bank. It tells the bank to give some of your money to someone. But you can only use a check if you have money in the bank!

A credit card is something people use when they want to pay later. Many people use a credit card to buy gas for their cars. Then they don't have to pay for the gas right away.

Some people think they are getting things free when they use a credit card. That isn't true at all. Even with a credit card, you have to pay for the things you buy! And sometimes you have to pay extra.

Now we know some of the things we use for money today.

We use money for money.

We use checks.

We use credit cards.

But even today some people still use barter—especially children.

# THE MUSICAL PALM TREE

Robert Barry

*illustrated by David Cunningham*

Pablito and Alicia stretched high on tiptoe and looked out over the warm wall of the roof terrace where they lived. "See. There she comes," Alicia cried, pointing to a puff of smoke on the horizon. "The cruise ship IS going to stop at Puerto Rico today."

"This is my last chance," said Pablito. "Tomorrow is the Fiesta Patronal. I must earn two dollars more to buy the beautiful Spanish *mantilla* for Mamá to wear to the Fiesta."

"I saw it this morning in the shop window," said Alicia. "¡Ay, *qué linda!* How beautiful! Mamá must have it."

Pablito popped a big straw *pava* on his head. "I have to be at the dock when the ship arrives," he called over his shoulder as he dashed down the old stone stairway.

He ran through the narrow street. At the corner he stopped and pressed his nose against the window of La Casa de Oro. It was the finest shop in all of San Juan. Pablito had never been inside, but he had heard his mother admire the *mantilla* in the window. "Only two dollars more," Pablito thought. "I must hurry."

The big white cruise ship was docking when he reached the pier. There was great excitement everywhere. Horns were tooting. Lines from the ship were being thrown ashore. A noisy crowd was gathering to meet the visitors.

Pablito fought for a place in line as the gangplank was lowered, and the visitors started to come ashore.

One of the guides shouted, "Let me take you to the beautiful beach at Luquillo."

Another called, "A trip to the mountains is better."

Pablito didn't say anything. Instead, he hoisted a little sign on a bamboo pole: LET PABLITO SHOW YOU PUERTO RICO—only 25¢.

223

A big man with broad shoulders laughed and asked, "What can you show an architect for twenty-five cents?"

Pablito lifted his *pava* and said, "*Bienvenido*, Señor. Welcome to Puerto Rico. An architect makes *casas grandes*, does he not?"

Pablito showed the architect some of the oldest buildings in San Juan. Then they went to see an ancient Spanish house that was being restored. Pablito ran up a winding stairway. "Look, Señor," he called, and nodded toward a tree that grew inside the patio.

"You could pick fruit for your breakfast each morning, right from this tree." Reaching out, Pablito picked a guava from the tree and tossed it down. "Wouldn't you like to live here?" he asked.

"Magnificent!" the architect exclaimed. He was so delighted with the old Spanish house he gave Pablito 25 cents, but he said that he wanted to stay and take some pictures.

Three sailors from the crew of the big ship were arguing on the dock when Pablito got back. They could not decide what they should see. The first sailor was pointing east. The second was pointing west. The third sailor was puffing great clouds of pipe smoke around them all.

"Ahoy, mates," Pablito cried. "Follow me and I'll show you just what a sailor should see in San Juan."

The three sailors quickly fell in line behind Pablito. One after the other, they marched to the little plaza at the entrance to the city.

"This is Plaza de Colón," said Pablito. "It is named after the greatest sailor of all, Christopher Columbus." The sailors took a closer look at the statue in the center of the plaza. "He discovered Puerto Rico, too," Pablito said proudly.

Pablito took the sailors to El Morro, the great Spanish fortress. He climbed on top of one of the big black cannons while the sailors gathered around him. "This fort was built

225

Pablito saw a crowd near the entrance to the big El Convento Hotel. In the center stood a small, dark-haired man with a cello. "My name is Sternstein," Pablito heard him say to some of the guides in the crowd. "I play the cello in the Symphony Orchestra. Eight hours' practice . . . every day . . . even on the cruise ship. Is there something for me to see in Puerto Rico? Something to hear . . . something soothing, musical . . . special?"

"I know a guitar player," one of the guides said. "He will play the most beautiful songs of the island for you."

"Oh no," Mr. Sternstein answered. "I have heard gypsy guitars played in Spanish caves. Surely his music cannot be better than that."

Another guide said, "I can take you to the beach at Boca de Cangrejos where the roar of the sea is like thunder."

"No, no," Mr. Sternstein answered impatiently. "I have heard the roar of the ocean on the rocks of Gay Head Light. Surely there is nothing to surpass that."

"Come with me to the rain forest," a third guide said. "There we can hear the song of the Puerto Rican Wood Warbler."

"I have heard the call of the Ruddy Red Quail Dove," said Mr. Sternstein. "What can be more beautiful than that?"

"I can show you a musical palm tree!" said Pablito.

"A palm tree . . . a musical palm tree!" Mr. Sternstein exclaimed. "That is something I have never seen—or heard."

"Come with me," said Pablito, and he took Mr. Sternstein by the hand. They hurried through the narrow streets, and along a narrow path that led out to the edge of the city.

They puffed up to the top of a steep hill.

"This is the musical palm tree," said Pablito, and he stopped before an enormous fan-shaped palm tree. "We must wait just a minute more. Let's rest, here under the tree."

They slumped down and leaned against the tree. The sun dropped slowly behind a range of misty mountaintops. The

# KIDS IN BUSINESS

## from NATIONAL GEOGRAPHIC WORLD

These boys and girls have found ways to make money and have fun doing it. Maybe you'd like to turn your talents into cash, too. What can you produce to sell? Or would you rather start an odd-jobs business? Ask family, neighbors, and friends to hire you for jobs that match your interests.

### A BUZZING BUSINESS IN ANIMALS

For a city boy, 14-year-old Jimmy Weill has an unusual business. Jimmy, who lives in Austin, Texas, raises animals—thousands of them! He says, "I have more than a hundred rabbits now and three beehives, with thousands of bees in each."

On the opposite page, Jimmy checks on his bees, a colony ready to protect its honey supply. He wears a mask and gloves to guard against stings. The bees fill the cells in the comb with nectar. Then they seal them with beeswax. The nectar soon changes into honey. "Then," says beekeeper Weill, "I cut open the wax cells with a hot knife and put the comb in a machine that extracts the honey."

Jimmy's dad helps him bottle the honey in eight-ounce jars. He sells it to neighbors for a dollar a jar. "In my first year of beekeeping," says Jimmy, "we sold about 150 pounds of honey." That's $300!

Jimmy also raises prizewinning rabbits. He started breeding and raising rabbits five years ago. Since then, his animals have won many trophies in state and national competitions. Jimmy says, "I breed my rabbits all year long, so I always have several young rabbits to pick from for the shows."

Imagine the wonderful smells when the Watson brothers take over their family's kitchen for their bread-baking business. Below, 12-year-old Ben, on the left, and 13-year-old Joseph prepare a bread order for customers. The brothers, from Sonora, California, started their business three years ago with help from their parents. They bake four to eight two-pound loaves a week for regular customers. Once for a fair, they baked two hundred loaves in two weeks.

"Our bread is all natural," says Joseph. Both boys help grind the flour from wheat. Joseph mixes the ingredients in a bread machine, and Ben forms the loaves in the pans. "Actually, you only have to work about ten minutes to make eight dollars," says Ben. "But the whole process takes an hour."

© James Sugar

© Joanne Kash

## A THREE-RING ENTERTAINER

She's a clown; she's an actress; she's a magician. Eleven-year-old KiKi Strickland, of South Daytona, Florida, loves to entertain. Above, she wears her clown costume and holds a look-alike porcelain doll. She also performs in television commercials. KiKi learned her first magic tricks from her parents. Today, she earns $125 for putting on a magic show. What's her favorite act? "I place a stuffed duck in a barrel," she says. "Then I wave a magic wand over it. Suddenly it becomes a live duck!" How? "Can you keep a secret?" asks KiKi. "Yes," says the audience. "So can I!" she replies.

## WASH-AND-WEAR ART PAINTED TO ORDER

Artist Arie Davis, 12, of Chicago, Illinois, paints clothes, not canvases. It takes Arie six hours to design and paint a sweatshirt, which sells for about $40. "I also paint sweatpants, hats, shoes, socks—anything anyone might want," he says. Arie began his business, City Sweats, two years ago. He keeps track of it with his home computer. "I like to do city scenes best, with joggers, cars, and buildings," says Arie.

"I started my business after I saw a bracelet that one of my mom's friends was wearing," says Ariane Finkel, 11. "I made one for myself. Then my mom wanted one, then her friend wanted one. . . . So it grew into a business." The New York City girl designs and makes jewelry from safety pins and beads strung on elastic. Ariane's creations sell for $26 to $40 in shops. "Business is great," says Ariane.

© Karen Keuhn, Matrix

237

# ALEXANDER, WHO USED TO BE RICH LAST SUNDAY

### Judith Viorst
### *illustrated by Ray Cruz*

It isn't fair that my brother Anthony has two dollars and three quarters and one dime and seven nickels and eighteen pennies.

It isn't fair that my brother Nicholas has one dollar and two quarters and five dimes and five nickels and thirteen pennies.

It isn't fair because what I've got is . . . bus tokens.

And most of the time what I've mostly got is . . . bus tokens.

And even when I'm very rich, I know that pretty soon what I'll have is . . . bus tokens.

I know because I used to be rich. Last Sunday.

Last Sunday Grandma Betty and Grandpa Louie came to visit from New Jersey. They brought lox because my father likes to eat lox. They brought plants because my mother likes to grow plants.

They brought a dollar for me and a dollar for Nick and a dollar for Anthony because—Mom says it isn't nice to say this—we like money.

A lot. Especially me.

My father told me to put the dollar away to pay for college.

He was kidding.

Anthony told me to use the dollar to go downtown to a store and buy a new face. Anthony stinks.

Nicky said to take the dollar and bury it in the garden and in a week a dollar tree would grow. Ha ha ha.

Mom said if I really want to buy a walkie-talkie, save my money.

239

Saving money is hard.

Because last Sunday, when I used to be rich, I went to Pearson's Drug Store and got bubble gum. And after the gum stopped tasting good, I got more gum. And after that gum stopped tasting good, I got more gum. And even though I told my friend David I'd sell him all the gum in my mouth for a nickel, he still wouldn't buy it.

Good-bye fifteen cents.

Last Sunday, when I used to be rich, I bet that I could hold my breath till 300. Anthony won. I bet that I could jump from the top of the stoop and land on my feet. Nicky won.

I bet that I could hide this purple marble in my hand, and my mom would never guess which hand I was hiding it in. I didn't know that moms made children pay.

Good-bye another fifteen cents.

I absolutely was saving the rest of my money. I positively was saving the rest of my money. Except that Eddie called me up and said that he would rent me his snake for an hour. I always wanted to rent his snake for an hour.

Good-bye twelve cents.

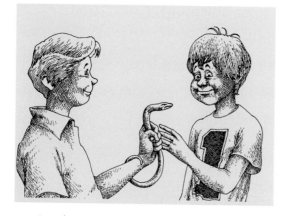

Anthony said when I'm ninety-nine I still won't have enough for a walkie-talkie. Nick said I'm too dumb to be let loose. My father said that there are certain words a boy can never say, no matter how ratty and mean his brothers are being. My father fined me five cents each for saying them.

Good-bye dime.

Last Sunday, when I used to be rich, by accident I flushed three cents down the toilet. A nickel fell through a crack when I walked on my hands. I tried to get my nickel out with a butter knife and also my mother's scissors.

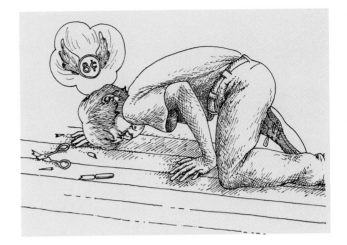

Good-bye eight cents.
And the butter knife.
And the scissors.

Last Sunday, when I used to be rich, I found this chocolate candy bar just sitting there. I rescued it from being melted or smushed. Except the way I rescued it from being melted or smushed was that I ate it. How was I supposed to know it was Anthony's?

Good-bye eleven cents.

241 🌸

I absolutely was saving the rest of my money. I positively was saving the rest of my money. But then Nick did a magic trick that made my pennies vanish in thin air. The trick to bring them back he hasn't learned yet.

Good-bye four cents.

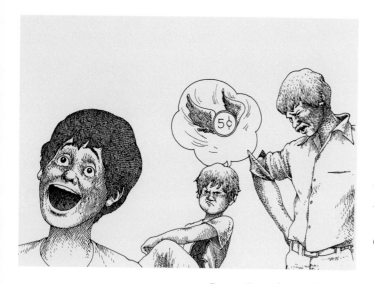

Anthony said that even when I'm 199, I still won't have enough for a walkie-talkie. Nick said they should lock me in a cage. My father said that there are certain things a boy can never kick, no matter how ratty and mean his brothers are being. My father made me pay five cents for kicking it.

Good-bye nickel.

Last Sunday, when I used to be rich, Cathy around the corner had a garage sale. I positively only went to look. I looked at a half-melted candle. I needed that candle. I looked at a bear with one eye. I needed that bear. I looked at a deck of cards that was perfect except for no seven of clubs and no two of diamonds. I didn't need that seven or that two.

Good-bye twenty cents.

I absolutely was saving the rest of my money. I positively was saving the rest of my money. I absolutely positively was saving the rest of my money. Except I needed to get some money to save.

I tried to make a tooth fall out—I could put it under my pillow and get a quarter. No loose teeth.

I looked in Pearson's telephone booths for nickels and dimes that people sometimes forget. No one forgot.

I brought some non-returnable bottles down to Friendly's Market. Friendly's Market wasn't very friendly.

I told my grandma and grandpa to come back soon.

Last Sunday, when I used to to be rich, I used to have a dollar. I do not have a dollar any more. I've got this dopey deck of cards. I've got this one-eyed bear. I've got this melted candle.

And . . . some bus tokens.

MEET JUDITH VIORST, AUTHOR

*Judith Viorst says many of her books are for or about her three children, Anthony, Nicholas, and Alexander. "I find my sons fierce and funny," she says, "and these qualities appear in many of my characters, some of whom are named after my boys."*

# FOUR DOLLARS AND FIFTY CENTS

### Eric A. Kimmel
### *illustrated by Glen Rounds*

I t's a terrible thing to call a cowboy a deadbeat, but in Shorty Long's case it was true. He owed everybody money, from Big Oscar the blacksmith to Widow Macrae, who ran the Silver Dollar Cafe and baked the best biscuits west of the Rockies.

"Shorty ain't a bad sort. He just hates to pay for anything he thinks he can get free," Big Oscar told the widow one afternoon over coffee at the Silver Dollar.

The widow brought Oscar another plate of biscuits. "How am I gonna keep this place going if folks won't pay their bills? Shorty's the worst. He owes me four dollars and fifty cents."

Big Oscar shook his head. "You got as much chance of collecting that money as seeing Custer ride back from the Little Bighorn."

Widow Macrae picked up her rolling pin. "That's what you think. I'm driving out to the Circle K this afternoon. If Shorty won't pay what he owes, I'll lay him out flatter 'n the bottom of a skillet."

As soon as Oscar left, Widow Macrae hitched her two horses, Clementine and Evangeline, to the buckboard and drove out to the Circle K ranch. Duck Pooley saw her coming. He rode back to the corral to warn Shorty.

"Widow Macrae's coming! She's got a rolling pin in her hand and an awful mean look in her eye. You better come up with that money, Shorty."

"Boys, you gotta help me!" Shorty yelped.

"Why don't you just pay what you owe?"

"It ain't that simple. If I paid the widow back, everybody I owe money to'd expect the same. I'd end up broker 'n a mess of eggs."

The Circle K boys decided to help Shorty out just for the fun of seeing what would happen. They knocked together a few boards to make a coffin. When Widow Macrae drove up, she found Shorty lying in it. He looked real peaceful. The Circle K boys stood around blubbering, wiping their noses on their sleeves.

Widow Macrae got down from the buckboard. "What happened to Shorty?" she asked.

"He's gone to the last roundup," the Circle K boys told her. "A bronco threw him. He landed on his head."

The widow leaned over for a closer look. Shorty looked deader 'n a Christmas tree in August. But she still wasn't sold, although she kept her suspicions to herself.

"Poor Shorty. It hurts my heart to see him like this. Where do you boys figure on burying him?"

"Why, here on the ranch. Somewheres."

Widow Macrae frowned. "That's not right. Shorty deserves better than sagebrush and coyotes. I know you don't have time to spare, what with the spring roundup coming on. But if you let me take Shorty back to town, I'll see he gets a decent burial."

The Circle K boys could hardly refuse.

"Then it's settled. Some of you boys load Shorty onto the buckboard. Try not to bounce him around too much."

"I'll nail the lid down," Duck Pooley volunteered.

"Not just yet," said Widow Macrae. "I want to see him one last time before I put him in the ground. Shorty Long was my friend."

That sure was news to Shorty. He didn't say a word, but he was thinking hard, mostly about what he'd like to do to Duck Pooley.

With the coffin loaded, Widow Macrae headed back towards town. She turned off onto the Boot Hill road. Boot Hill is where they bury cowboys like Shorty, who die with their boots on. It's a mighty rough road for a feller's last journey.

Widow Macrae reined in at the top of the hill next to a freshly dug grave. She got down from the buckboard, unhitched the horses, and turned them loose to graze. Then she took hold of the coffin and dragged it out of the wagon. Shorty saw stars when the coffin hit the ground, but he was bound and determined not to pay that four dollars and fifty cents, so he lay still.

The widow studied him hard. "Can you hear me, Shorty? If you can, listen good. I don't know if you're dead or not, but I'm gonna keep my eyes on you all night. If you ain't moved by morning, into the ground you go!"

247

Poor Shorty! It was pay up or be buried alive—and he couldn't make up his mind which was worse! The sun went down. With Widow Macrae's eyes fixed on him tight, Shorty lay still in his coffin, not moving a muscle, not hardly breathing, waiting for something to happen.

On about midnight something did. Riders! He heard them coming up the Boot Hill road. Widow Macrae ducked behind a tombstone. As for Shorty, he was sure it was a posse of dead cowboys riding back from the grave for one last roundup. He lay in his coffin, stiff as rawhide, hoping that with all the graves up there they wouldn't notice one extra corpse.

Three riders reined in at the top of Boot Hill. They got off their horses. One lit a lantern while the other two lugged an iron strongbox over to the open grave. Anyone would recognize them at once. It was Big Nose George

Parrott and two of his gang, Smiley Dunlap and the Oregon Kid. The outlaws started bragging about a train they robbed that afternoon. They came to the graveyard to divide the loot. No one would think of looking for outlaws on Boot Hill. Not live ones, anyway.

Shorty was in a heap of trouble. If those outlaws caught him spying on them, he wouldn't have to worry about being a fake corpse. Big Nose George drew his six-gun.

"Stand back, boys! I'll settle this business!"

He fired a shot into the strongbox padlock. Shorty nearly gave up the ghost. He thought that bullet was meant for him.

"Yahoo! We struck it rich!"

The Oregon Kid kicked open the lid. He and Smiley reached inside and began throwing fistfuls of hundred dollar bills into the air. That made Big Nose George real mad.

"Quit that clowning! This ain't the circus! You boys pick up them greenbacks and put 'em back where you found 'em!"

"Aw, George!"

"Aw, George nothing! We're gonna divvy it up business-like. No grabbing!"

The Kid and Smiley started picking up the money. One of the bills landed in Shorty's coffin.

"Holy Hannah! What's this? There's a dead 'un here!"

"Don't drop your britches, boys. Dead 'uns don't bite." Big Nose George moseyed over for a closer look. "Why, it's some

poor cowpoke whose burying had to wait till morning.
They should've covered him up, though. It ain't decent
leaving a feller out in the open where the buzzards can get
at him. But that ain't none of our concern. Bring over them
bills and let's get started."

"Can't we close that coffin first?" the Kid asked. "Dead
'uns give me the willies."

"Sure, go ahead," said Big Nose George.

The Kid slammed the coffin lid right down on Shorty's
nose! Tears came to Shorty's eyes. He clenched his teeth to
keep from yelling.

"What's the matter?" Smiley asked.

"This lid don't fit."

"Let me try." Smiley sat down hard on the coffin. He
packed a lot of weight. The lid mashed Shorty's nose into
his face. Shorty saw stars, but not the ones in the sky.

"What's keeping you two?" Big Nose George growled.

"This lid won't lay flat."

"Let me see." Big Nose George had a look. "Are you both crack-brained? Use your eyes. This feller's nose sticks up a mile. It's way too long for the coffin."

"What'll we do?"

"Easy! He don't need a sniffer where he's going. I'll cut it off with my bowie knife!"

That was enough for Shorty. He sat up in his coffin and hollered, "Hold on, boys! I ain't that dead!"

Big Nose George nearly dropped his teeth.

Smiley let out a yell as the whole gang ran for their horses.

Those outlaws shot out of that graveyard faster than fireworks!

Widow Macrae laughed fit to bust. When she was all laughed out, she came from behind the tombstone and gave Shorty the scolding of his life.

"I hope you learned your lesson. You nearly got your nose cut off for four dollars and fifty cents!"

Shorty was too embarrassed to say anything. He and Widow Macrae gathered up the money the outlaws left behind. In the morning they took it to the railroad agent in

town. He gave them a five-hundred-dollar reward to divide between them.

Shorty rubbed his nose. "I reckon we're even now."

"Not quite," said Widow Macrae. "You still owe me four dollars and fifty cents."

Shorty stared glumly at his pile of fifty-dollar bills. "I don't have no change. How about if I come by tomorrow and settle up?"

"I'll expect you," Widow Macrae said.

But so far as anyone knows, he hasn't paid her yet.

## MEET ERIC A. KIMMEL, AUTHOR

*"I like to knit. My friend Alma taught me how. From the first time I picked up the needles, I knew—Hey! I can do this! Since then I've knitted dozens of sweaters. It takes about a year to complete each one, and I knit them in the traditional way, in the round, all in one piece. The truth is they are quite simple to do if you know the two basic knitting stitches, knit and purl. Aside from that, it's just a matter of paying attention to what you're doing and knitting one stitch at a time.*

253

*"My writing is like knitting. I love the rich textures of traditional tales, but I also make sure to put something of myself into every story. Stories are like sweaters. They grow word by word, stitch by stitch. Sometimes that takes a long time, but time really doesn't matter. The work takes as long as it takes, and when it's done, it's done. I give most of my sweaters away. They are made to be worn and enjoyed, not locked in a closet, covered with mothballs. Publishing a story is also like giving it away. My hope is that people will read and enjoy it. Don't forget, stories work just as well as thick sweaters for keeping you warm on cold winter nights."*

# FINE ART
## MONEY

254

*80 Two-Dollar Bills (front and rear).* 1962. Andy Warhol.

Silkscreen on canvas. Museum Ludwig, Cologne. © Andy Warhol Foundation
for the Visual Arts. Photo: Rheinisches Bildarchive

*The Money Lender and His Wife.* 1514. Quentin Matsys.

Tempera and oil on wood. The Louvre, Paris. Photo: Erich Lessing/Art Resource

*255* 🍃

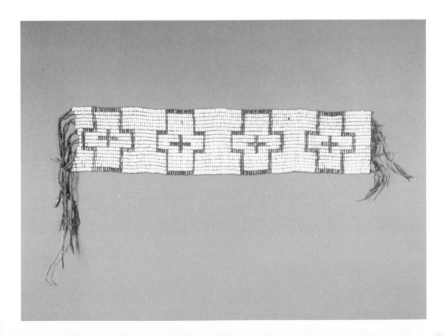

Wampum belt. 1650–1800. Iroquois.

The National Museum of the American Indian,
Smithsonian Institution. 2431

# SMART
## Shel Silverstein

My dad gave me one dollar bill
'Cause I'm his smartest son,
And I swapped it for two shiny quarters
'Cause two is more than one!

And then I took the quarters
And traded them to Lou
For three dimes—I guess he don't know
That three is more than two!

Just then, along came old blind Bates
And just 'cause he can't see
He gave me four nickels for my three dimes,
And four is more than three!

And I took the nickels to Hiram Coombs
Down at the seed-feed store,
And the fool gave me five pennies for them,
And five is more than four!

And then I went and showed my dad,
And he got red in the cheeks
And closed his eyes and shook his head—
Too proud of me to speak!

# TONY AND THE QUARTER

Jack Prelutsky
*illustrated by Victoria Chess*

Tony's my neighbor
and Tony's my friend.
Today Tony's ma
gave him money to spend.

He slapped my behind
and he said with a laugh,
"Whatever I get,
you can have almost half.

I got a whole quarter,
I'll split it with you.
Let's go get some candy
and bubble gum too."

So happily downhill
the two of us tore,
to see what a quarter
would buy at the store.

But things didn't work
just the way that we planned,
Tony tripped—and the quarter
flew out of his hand.

It rolled down the sidewalk
and oh, what a pain!
We couldn't catch up
and it went down the drain.

Such a dumb thing to do,
oh, it made me so sore.
Still, I guess I like Tony
as much as before.

# THE COBBLER'S SONG

### adapted and illustrated
### by Marcia Sewall

O nce upon a time a poor cobbler lived in the basement of a large house in Paris. He had to work from early morning until late at night to make enough money to keep himself and his wife and children. But he was happy in his dark little rooms, and he sang all day as he mended old shoes.

On the floor above him lived a very rich man. His rooms were large and sunny. He wore fine clothes and had plenty of good things to eat. Still, he was never happy.

All night long he lay awake thinking about his money— how to make more, or fearing lest it be stolen. Often the sun was shining in at his windows before he fell asleep.

Now, as soon as it grew light enough to see, the cobbler always got up and went about his work. And as he hammered, he sang. His songs floated up to the rooms of the rich man and woke him.

"This is just dreadful!" said the rich man. "I cannot sleep at night for thinking of my money, and I cannot sleep in the daytime because of the singing of that silly cobbler."

So the rich man sat down and thought the matter over.

"Hmm," he said to himself, "if the cobbler had something to worry about, he would not sing so much. I must think of a plan to stop him. Let me see, what worries men most?

"Why money, to be sure! Some men worry because they have so little. The cobbler has little enough, it's true, but that does not worry him. In fact, he is the happiest man I know.

"Other men worry because they have too much money, which is my trouble. I wonder if it would worry the cobbler if he had too much. That's the idea! Now I know what I shall do!"

259

A few minutes later, the rich man entered the cobbler's poor home.

"What can I do for you?" asked the cobbler, recognizing his neighbor but wondering why so fine a man should enter his little shop.

"Here, I have brought you a present," said the rich man, and he gave the poor man a purse.

The cobbler opened it and saw that it was full of shining gold pieces.

"I cannot take all this money!" cried he. "I have not earned it. Take it back."

"No," answered the rich man, "you have earned it by your songs. I give it to you because you are the happiest man I know."

Without waiting for any thanks, the rich man left the shop.

The cobbler turned the gold pieces out on his table and began to count them. He had counted to fifty-two, when he looked up and saw a man passing by the window. He quickly hid the gold. Then he went into the bedroom to count it where no one could see him.

He piled the coins up on the bed. How golden they were! How bright! He had never seen so much money before. He looked and looked at the money until everything in the room seemed golden and bright. Then he counted it slowly.

"One hundred pieces of gold! How rich I am! Where shall I hide it for safekeeping?"

First he hid the coins under the covers at the foot of the bed, which he could see from his workbench.

"The money makes quite a lump under the covers," he said. "Perhaps someone else will see it and steal it. I think I should hide it under the pillow."

While he was putting it under the pillow, his wife came into the room.

"What is the matter with the bed?" she asked.

The cobbler glared at her, and drove her from the room with angry words—the first cross words he had ever spoken to her.

Dinner came, but he could not eat a mouthful because he was afraid someone would steal his treasure while he was at the table! As he worked, not a note did he sing. By suppertime he felt worse. Not a kind word did he speak to his wife.

Day after day and night after night, the cobbler grew more and more unhappy, worrying about his money. He dared not go to sleep, lest he should wake to find that his gold had disappeared. He tossed and turned on his pillow.

But upstairs, the rich man was happy. "That was a fine idea," he said to himself drowsily. "Now I can sleep all day without being awakened by the cobbler's song."

For a month, the cobbler worried over the hundred gold pieces. He grew thin and pale, and his wife and children were most unhappy. At last he could bear the worry no longer, so he called his wife and told her the whole story.

"Dear husband," she said, "take back the gold. All the gold in the world is not worth as much to me as your happiness and one of your glad songs."

How relieved the cobbler felt to hear her say this. He picked up the purse and ran upstairs to the rich man's home. Throwing the gold on the table, he smiled and said: "Here is your purse of gold. Take it back! I can live without your money, but I cannot live without my song."

### MEET MARCIA SEWALL, AUTHOR AND ILLUSTRATOR

*About illustrating* The Cobbler's Song
*Sewall says: "What an absolute joy it was to sit down and paint, and use colors that seemed to express the changing moods of the story. I used gouache which is an opaque watercolor paint not unlike poster paint. The story is a variation of the old rich man, poor man theme. It deals with feelings, so it made sense to use full-color and to put paint on expressively."*

# THE GOLDEN TOUCH

*illustrated by Rebecca Guay*

In the kingdom of Phrygia in Asia Minor there once lived a very rich king whose name was Midas. There were two things King Midas loved more than anything else in the world: his gold and his young daughter.

The king spent long hours in his dark treasure house, counting his gold. But no matter how much gold he had, it was never enough for him.

One day an old, weary traveler came to his palace, and Midas himself gave the man food and drink and a place to rest. Not long after, as Midas sat in his gloomy treasure house, a dazzling young man came through the narrow window, riding a sunbeam, and stood before him.

It was Bacchus, the god of the vine. The weary traveler had been Bacchus's teacher, and the god was grateful for Midas's kindness to his friend. Bacchus looked around the room and said, "What a wealthy man you must be, with so much gold."

"That is true," said the king, "but there is not so much gold here as there could be."

"What would satisfy you?" asked Bacchus. "Name the deepest wish of your heart, Midas, and it shall be granted."

Midas had often dreamed of what he would ask for if ever he had such a chance, and so at once he answered, "Oh, Bacchus, let everything I touch be turned to gold."

The god frowned. "You have chosen foolishly, Midas. Nevertheless, I have promised. At sunrise your wish will come true." Then Bacchus vanished.

The next morning Midas sprang out of bed, eager to test his power. First he touched his favorite book of poems, which lay on the table beside his bed. At once the words faded and the book turned to gold. Midas was startled at first and then thrilled.

As he put on his clothes, they too turned to gold. Wearing the heavy garments, Midas went out into his rose garden. As if in a trance he moved from bush to bush, changing each blossom and bud, leaf and branch to gold. As the color and fragrance of the living roses faded, a chill came over Midas. Hurriedly he went inside to eat breakfast.

As Midas picked up his knife to peel his orange, both knife and orange were changed to gold. When he bit into his bread, he got only a mouthful of golden crumbs. How on earth, he began to wonder, am I ever going to eat or drink anything?

Just then his little daughter came into the room, crying bitterly. In her hand she held two of the golden roses.

"What is the matter, dear child?" Midas asked. "Don't the wonderful roses please you?"

"They are not wonderful," sobbed the child. "They're cold and hard and have no sweet smell. They're ugly!"

Worried, King Midas stretched out his arm to comfort his daughter. But even as he touched her, she too hardened into gold. From the soles of her brown sandals to the curls of her brown hair, the child became a golden statue with golden tears on its cheeks.

Now Midas knew how wrong he had been. He cursed himself for his greed, wept for his child, and prayed that Bacchus would take away his unhappy gift.

Bacchus was merciful. He appeared once more in a shaft of sunlight and said, "You are wiser than you were, King Midas. Go now to the River Pactolus. Its water will wash away the Golden Touch. A few drops of this water will restore the things you have turned to gold."

Midas bowed low, and when he looked up, Bacchus was gone. Midas hurried to the river and plunged in. He quenched his thirst with the pure water. Then he took up a clay pitcher that stood on the river bank. To his great relief, the pitcher remained clay. He filled it with water and ran to pour some on the golden statue that was his daughter. As life returned to her, joy returned to the king's heart.

Together the two poured the life-giving water over the golden garden, and together they laughed as color and fragrance came back to the roses.

Thereafter, King Midas lived a simple life. He hated gold and loved only the gifts of the earth and the pleasures of human company. Only one thing remains to recall Midas's folly. To this day the sands of the River Pactolus glisten golden in the sun. And if you bend low over the river bank, you can hear the waters murmur:

> Treasures lost and pleasures found,
> Here the Golden Touch was drowned.

269

# BIBLIOGRAPHY

*Arthur's Funny Money* by Lillian Hoban. Find out how Arthur and his sister Violet go into business and solve both Violet's math problem and Arthur's financial problem.

*The Cat Who Loved to Sing* by Nonny Hogrogian. A tuneful cat trades one thing for another until he finally gets a very useful gift.

*The Chocolate Touch* by Patrick Skene Catling. Would you want a chocolate touch? You're sure to enjoy this fun twist on the King Midas tale.

*Faces*, September 1988. The entire issue of this month's magazine is devoted to money—what it is, how it's used in various cultures around the world, and fascinating facts about money laws that once determined fees and salaries.

270

*The Go-Around Dollar* by Barbara Johnston Adams. You'll have fun following the travels of a one-dollar bill as you read this fictional story sprinkled with facts and amusing tales.

*If You Made a Million* by David M. Schwartz. Explore the world of money in a fanciful way. Learn about what you can do with the money you earn and choices you'll have to make.

*Make Four Million Dollars by Next Thursday* by Stephen Manes. Jason finds a get-rich-quick book and attracts much attention when he begins to follow its crazy advice.

*The Money Tree* by Sarah Stewart. A mysterious tree sprouts and grows in Miss McGillicuddy's yard—a money tree. She is startled by the crowds that gather. What will she do?

# GLOSSARY

| PRONUNCIATION KEY |
|---|

**a** as in **at**  **o** as in **ox**  **ou** as in **out**  **ch** as in **chair**
**ā** as in **late**  **ō** as in **rose**  **u** as in **up**  **hw** as in **which**
**â** as in **care**  **ô** as in **bought**  **ûr** as in **turn;**  **ng** as in **ring**
**ä** as in **father**    and **raw**    **germ, learn,**  **sh** as in **shop**
**e** as in **set**  **oi** as in **coin**    **firm, work**  **th** as in **thin**
**ē** as in **me**  **o͞o** as in **book**  **ə** as in **about,**  **t͟h** as in **there**
**i** as in **it**  **o͞o** as in **too**    **chicken, pencil,**  **zh** as in **treasure**
**ī** as in **kite**  **or** as in **form**    **cannon, circus**

The mark (ˊ) is placed after a syllable with a heavy accent,
as in **chicken** (chikˊ ən).
The mark (ˊ) after a syllable shows a lighter accent,
as in **disappear** (disˊ ə pērˊ).

**absolutely** (abˊ sə lo͞otˊ lē) *adv.*
Certainly; for sure.

**abuse** (ə byo͞osˊ) *n.* Unkind or cruel
words or actions.

**amber** (amˊ bər) *n.* A yellowish-brown
color.

**amethyst** (amˊ ə thist) *n.* A purple
color.

**amuse** (ə myo͞ozˊ) *v.* To please.

**annoy** (ə noiˊ) *v.* To disturb; to make
angry.

**ao dai** (ow zī) *n. Vietnamese.* A
garment worn by females in Vietnam,
usually for special occasions.

**apathetic** (apˊ ə thetˊ ik) *adj.* Not
interested; not caring about
something.

**appoint** (ə pointˊ) *v.* To name or
select.

**appointed** (ə poinˊ tid) *adj.* Set; agreed
upon.

**approach** (ə prōchˊ) *v.* To come near.

**architect** (ärˊ ki tektˊ) *n.* A person
who designs buildings.

**architecture** (ärˊ ki tekˊ chər) *n.* The
science or art of designing buildings.

**astonish** (ə stonˊ ish) *v.* To surprise; to
amaze.

**astronomy** (ə stronˊ ə mē) *n.* The
science of studying the stars and
planets.

**auburn** (ôˊ bərn) *adj.* Reddish-brown.

273 🧷

**Pronunciation Key:** at; lāte; câre; fäther; set; mē; it; kīte; ox; rōse; ô in bought; coin; bŏŏk; tōō; form; out; up; tûrn; ə sound in about, chicken, pencil, cannon, circus; chair; hw in which; ring; shop; thin; there; zh in treasure.

**audible** (ô′ də bəl) *adj.* Loud enough to be heard.

**baby-sitter** (bā′ bē sit′ ər) *n.* A person who takes care of a child when the child's parents are not home.

**bandit** (ban′ dit) *n.* A robber; a thief.

**banister** (ban′ ə stər) *n.* The railing on a staircase.

**bawl** (bôl) *v.* To yell loudly; to cry out.

**befallen** (bi fôl′ ən) *v.* A past tense of **befall:** To happen to.

**biology** (bī ol′ ə jē) *n.* The science of studying plants and animals.

**bitterly** (bit′ ər lē) *adv.* With anger and sadness at the same time.

**blacksmith** (blak′ smith′) *n.* A person who makes horseshoes.

**blunt** (blunt) *adj.* Having a dull or thick edge.

**botany** (bot′ n ē) *n.* The science of studying plants.

**bowie knife** (bō′ ē nīf′) *n.* A thick-handled knife named for James Bowie.

**Braille** (brāl) *n.* A system of printing with raised dots that stand for letters. Blind people read Braille by touching the dots.

**breadbox** (bred′ boks′) *n.* A special box for keeping bread fresh.

**breed** (brēd) *v.* To raise animals.

**bridle** (brīd′ l) *n.* The part of a horse's harness that goes over its head.

**brilliant** (bril′ yənt) *adj.* Sparkling.

**britches** (brich′ iz) *n.* Breeches; pants; trousers.

**bronco** (brong′ kō) *n.* A wild horse.

**buckboard** (buk′ bord′) *n.* A horse-drawn carriage made from a long, wooden board or simple frame.

**calico** (kal′ i kō) *n.* A type of cotton cloth with bright-colored patterns.

**canopy** (kan′ ə pē) *n.* An overhead covering.

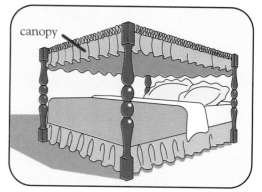

canopy

**card** (kärd) *v.* To comb wool.

**cartwheel** (kärt´hwēl´) *n.* A jump made by landing on the hands and then the feet, turning like a wheel.

***casa grande*** (kä´sä grän´dä) *n. Spanish.* A great house.

**catnip** (kat´nip) *n.* A spicy-smelling plant that cats like.

**cello** (chel´ō) *n.* A musical instrument that looks like a large violin. It is held with one end on the floor.

**champion** (cham´pē ən) *n.* A person who protects others or fights for others.

**chant** (chant) *v.* To sing or repeat words as a group.

***chao buoi sang*** (chow bwē sung) *Vietnamese.* Good morning.

**chemistry** (kem´ə strē) *n.* The science of studying what different substances are made of.

**chisel** (chiz´əl) *v.* To cut with a metal tool.

chisel

**chive** (chīv) *n.* A small plant related to leeks and onions.

**circulate** (sûr´kyə lāt´) *v.* To pass around.

**clench** (klench) *v.* To close the teeth or fingers tightly.

**coax** (kōks) *v.* To encourage.

**cobbler** (kob´lər) *n.* A person who repairs shoes and boots.

**coffin** (kô´fin) *n.* The box in which a dead body is buried.

**colonel** (kûr´nl) *n.* An officer in the army, marines, or air force.

**commotion** (kə mō´shən) *n.* A disturbance; a fuss; a lot of noise and confusion.

**companion** (kəm pan´yən) *n.* A friend; someone who goes along or in company with someone else.

**compete** (kəm pēt´) *v.* To try to win by striving against another person or people.

**competition** (kom´pi tish´ən) *n.* A contest.

**controversial** (kon´trə vûr´shəl) *adj.* Causing arguments or different opinions.

**corpse** (korps) *n.* A dead body.

**corral** (kə ral´) *n.* A fenced-in area for cattle or horses.

**creed** (krēd) *n.* The statement of a person's belief or faith.

**cringe** (krinj) *v.* To back away from something unpleasant; to shrink back; to crouch.

275

**Pronunciation Key:** at; lāte; câre; fäther; set; mē; it; kīte; ox; rōse; ô in bought; coin; bŏŏk; tōō; form; out; up; tûrn; ə sound in about, chicken, pencil, cannon, circus; chair; hw in which; ring; shop; thin; there; zh in treasure.

**crinkle** (kring′ kəl) *v.* 1. To wrinkle. 2. To make tiny, sharp sounds.

**crossbow** (krôs′ bō′) *n.* An ancient weapon that looks like a bow and arrow but with a wooden strip across the center of the bow.

**crouch** (krouch) *v.* To bend down with knees bent.

**cruise** (krōōz) *n.* A voyage taken on a ship for pleasure.

**cubism** (kyōō′ biz əm) *n.* A style of painting in which the picture is formed by cubes or square shapes.

**curse** (kûrs) *v.* To say that bad things should happen to someone.

**dahlia** (dal′ yə) *n.* A plant with showy, bright-colored flowers.

**dangle** (dang′ gəl) *v.* To hang down loosely.

**dazzle** (daz′ əl) *v.* To blind with bright light.

**deadbeat** (ded′ bēt′) *n.* A person who owes money and doesn't pay.

**debt** (det) *n.* 1. Money that is owed. 2. The condition of owing money.

**deceive** (di sēv′) *v.* To trick; to cheat.

**decent** (dē′ sənt) *adj.* Proper.

**despair** (di spâr′) *n.* A lack of hope.

**despite** (di spīt′) *prep.* In spite of; regardless of.

**disgrace** (dis grās′) *v.* To act badly; to shame.

**dispute** (di spyōōt′) *v.* To argue; to quarrel.

**divvy** (div′ ē) *v.* To divide for sharing.

**dollop** (dol′ əp) *n.* A blob of something; a small amount of something.

**doomed** (dōōmd) *adj.* Certain to come to a bad end; sure to die.

**dreadful** (dred′ fəl) *adj.* Terrible; very bad.

**dredger** (drej′ ər) *n.* A machine that scoops mud from a river bottom.

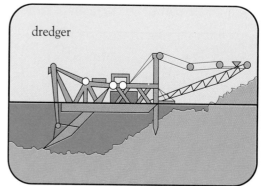

**drowsily** (drou′ zə lē) *adv.* Sleepily; in a sleepy way.

276

**eaves** (ēvz) *n. pl.* The overhanging lower edges of a roof.

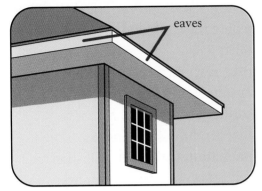

**encourage** (en kûr´ ij) *v.* To urge or inspire someone to do something.

**entertain** (en´ tər tān´) *v.* To amuse.

**extract** (ik strakt´) *v.* To draw or pull out.

**extraordinary** (ik stror´ dn er´ ē) *adj.* Rare; not ordinary.

**fiesta** (fē es´ tə) *n.* A festival; a celebration.

**flannel** (flan´ l) *n.* A warm, soft material made of wool or cotton.

**flat** (flat) *n.* A musical note that sounds one-half tone lower than it usually does.

**flatter** (flat´ ər) *adj.* More flat.

**folly** (fol´ ) *n.* A lack of good sense; foolishness.

**ford** (ford) *v.* To cross a river or stream.

**forecast** (for´ kast´) *v.* To tell what will happen.

**forefeet** (for´ fēt´) *n.* Plural of **forefoot:** One of the front feet of a four-legged animal.

**fortress** (for´ tris) *n.* A fort; a place to stay safe.

**fragrance** (frā´ grəns) *n.* A sweet smell.

**fugitive** (fyōō´ ji tiv) *n.* A person or animal who runs away.

**gamble** (gam´ bəl) *n.* A risk; a chance.

**garment** (gär´ mənt) *n.* An article of clothing.

**garnet** (gär´ nit) *n.* A deep red jewel.

**greasewood** (grēs´ wŏŏd´) *n.* A woody plant that grows in the dry West.

**grim** (grim) *adj.* Stern; harsh.

**grope** (grōp) *v.* To seek or feel blindly.

**guava** (gwä´ və) *n.* A large, yellow tropical fruit.

**gutter** (gut´ ər) *n.* A curved path or trough for carrying off rain water.

**haunch** (hônch) *n.* The hip and the thickest part of the thigh.

**hawthorn** (hô´ thorn´) *n.* A thorny shrub with red or white flowers.

*277*

**hearsay** (hēr´ sā´) *n.* A rumor; information heard from someone but not proved.

**hearth** (härth) *n.* The floor of a fireplace.

**hedge** (hej) *n.* A row of bushes used as a fence.

**hinge** (hinj) *n.* A metal joint that attaches a door to its frame and lets the door move.

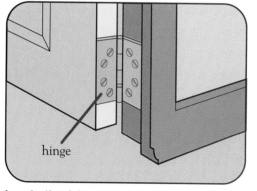

hinge

**hitch** (hich) *v.* To fasten with a loop or a hook.

**hoa-phuong** (hwä fung) *n.* *Vietnamese.* A tropical flower in Vietnam that has groups of red blossoms.

**hoist** (hoist) *v.* To lift up; to raise.

**holler** (hol´ ər) *v.* To yell.

**honorable** (on´ ər ə bəl) *adj.* Honest; having high standards; trustworthy.

**horizon** (hə rī´ zən) *n.* The distant line where the earth and the sky seem to meet.

**host** (hōst) *n.* Someone who entertains guests.

**hostility** (ho stil´ i tē) *n.* Unfriendliness; willingness to fight.

**humiliation** (hyōō mil´ ē ā´ shən) *n.* An action or event that hurts someone's pride.

**hydraulics** (hī drô´ liks) *n.* The science of studying liquids that are in motion.

**imagination** (i maj´ ə nā´ shən) *n.* The ability to create new ideas in one's mind.

**imitate** (im´ i tāt´) *v.* To copy.

**inclined** (in klīnd´) *adj.* Usually wants to do something.

**Indostan** (in´ də stan) *n.* An old-time name for India and Pakistan combined.

**ingredient** (in grē´ dē ənt) *n.* One of the materials in a mixture.

**initially** (i nish´ əl lē) *adv.* At first.

**inquire** (in kwīr´) *v.* To question; to ask.

**intimidate** (in tim´ i dāt´) *v.* To threaten; to try to scare.

278

**iron hand** (ī´ ərn hand´) *idiom.* In a strict way.

**jakered** (jāk´ ərd) *v.* To be surprised or to be fooled.

**jangle** (jang´ gəl) *v.* To make a harsh sound, like two pieces of metal hitting each other.

**jiggle** (jig´ əl) *v.* To move back and forth quickly.

**kip** (kip) *n.* A nap; sleep.

**latch-string** (lach´ string´) *n.* A string that goes through a hole in a door to keep the door closed.

**launch** (lônch) *v.* To begin.

**leek** (lēk) *n.* A plant that is similar to a green onion.

**lingonberry** (ling´ ən ber´ ē) *n.* A bright red berry related to the cranberry.

**lope** (lōp) *v.* To take long steps while running.

**lox** (loks) *n.* A form of salmon for eating.

**loyalty** (loi´ əl tē) *n.* Faithfulness; support for another person.

**lug** (lug) *v.* To pull; to drag.

**lump** (lump) *n.* A piece; a chunk.

**lunge** (lunj) *v.* To leap forward at someone.

**lurk** (lûrk) *v.* To hide.

**lute** (lo͞ot) *n.* An old-time string instrument with a pear shape and a bent neck, played by plucking its strings.

lute

279

**mantilla** (män tē´ yä) *n. Spanish.* A veil of silk and lace.

**margin** (mär´ jin) *n.* The blank edge of a paper.

**marvel** (mär´ vəl) *n.* A wonderful or amazing thing.

**matchless** (mach´ lis) *adj.* The best.

**measurement** (mezh´ ər mənt) *n.* The size of something.

**merciful** (mûr´ si fəl) *adj.* Forgiving; kind.

**mercy** (mûr´ sē) *n.* Forgiveness.

**metallurgy** (met´ l ûr´ jē) *n*. The science of heating or working with metals.

**micky** (mik´ ē) *n*. A potato.

**miserable** (miz´ ər ə bəl) *adj*. Very unhappy.

**misfortune** (mis for´ chən) *n*. Bad luck; disaster.

**mock** (mok) *v*. To make fun of.

**monument** (mon´ yə mənt) *n*. Anything built to honor a person or event.

monument

**mosey** (mō´ zē) *v*. To walk slowly; to stroll.

**mothball** (môth´ bôl´) *n*. A small ball of strong-smelling chemicals put in closets to keep moths away from clothes.

**muffler** (muf´ lər) *n*. A scarf worn for warmth.

**mustache** (mus´ tash) *n*. Hair grown on the upper lip.

**nectar** (nek´ tər) *n*. The sweet liquid found in flowers, used by bees to make honey.

**notion** (nō´ shən) *n*. An idea.

**nudge** (nuj) *v*. To push; to poke.

**observation** (ob´ zûr vā´ shən) *n*. The act of studying or noticing.

**ocotillo** (ō´ kə tēl´ yō) *n*. A desert bush with sharp spines.

**opportunity** (op´ ər tōō´ ni tē) *n*. A good chance.

**organization** (or´ gə nə zā´ shən) *n*. A group of people who join together for one purpose; a club.

**originality** (ə rij´ ə nal´ i tē) *n*. Newness; freshness.

**padlock** (pad´ lok´) *n*. A lock that can be taken off and put back on by unlocking a curved piece of metal.

**paling** (pā´ ling) *n*. A long pointed pole, part of a fence.

**parcel** (pär´ səl) *n.* A bundle; a package.

**pastelillo** (päs tā lē´ yō) *n. Spanish.* A pastry baked with meat or cheese inside.

**patiently** (pā´ shənt lē) *adv.* Without complaining.

**patio** (pat´ ē ō´) *n.* An inner courtyard open to the sky.

**pattern** (pat´ ərn) *n.* A model to follow when making clothes.

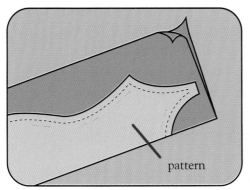
pattern

**pava** (pä´ vä) *n. Spanish.* A large straw hat.

**period** (pēr´ ē əd) *n.* An amount of time.

**persuade** (pər swād´) *v.* To convince; to talk someone into agreeing.

**petition** (pə tish´ ən) *n.* A written request to someone in charge, signed by those who agree.

**physics** (fiz´ iks) *n.* The science of studying the actions of natural forces.

**pier** (pēr) *n.* A landing place built out over water.

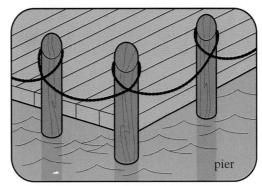
pier

**pitch** (pich) *n.* A dark, sticky substance used to make things waterproof.

**plaza** (plä´ zə) *n.* A public space or square in a city.

**porcelain** (por´ sə lin) *n.* A fine, delicate china.

**positively** (poz´ i tiv lē) *adv.* Certainly; for sure.

**posse** (pos´ ē) *n.* A group of people who gather to help a sheriff, usually on horses.

**possess** (pə zes´) *v.* To have; to own.

**prejudice** (prej´ ə dis) *n.* Unfairness; an opinion formed without knowing the facts.

**prey** (prā) *n.* An animal that is hunted to be eaten.

**prickle** (prik´ əl) *v.* To tingle or sting slightly.

281

**Pronunciation Key:** at; lāte; câre; fäther; set; mē; it; kīte; ox; rōse; ô in bought; coin; bŏŏk; tōō; form; out; up; tûrn; ə sound in about, chicken, pencil, cannon, circus; **ch**air; **hw** in **wh**ich; ri**ng**; **sh**op; **th**in; **th**ere; **zh** in trea**s**ure.

**privet** (priv´ it) *n.* A shrub related to the lilac bush and the olive tree. It has small white flowers and smooth, dark fruit; all parts are poisonous.

**proclaim** (prō klām´) *v.* To announce publicly.

**provoke** (prə vōk´) *v.* To cause.

**Queen Anne's lace** (kwēn´ anz´ lās´) *n.* A wild form of the carrot plant with lacy white flowers.

**quench** (kwench) *v.* To end a thirst; to satisfy.

**quiver** (kwiv´ ər) *v.* To shake slightly.

**quoth** (kwōth) *v. archaic.* Said.

**rabbi** (rab´ ī) *n.* A teacher of Jewish law and religion.

**racial** (rā´ shəl) *adj.* Having to do with a race of people.

282

**rafter** (raf´ tər) *n.* One of the beams that hold a roof.

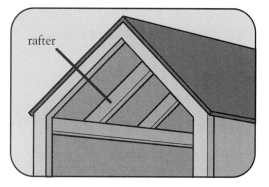

rafter

**rawhide** (rô´ hīd´) *n.* A piece of cattle hide, or skin, that has not been tanned, or turned into leather.

**reasonable** (rē´ zə nə bəl) *adj.* Having normal thoughts; using good judgment.

**reckon** (rek´ ən) *v.* To think; to suppose.

**reflection** (ri flek´ shən) *n.* An image or likeness seen in a surface such as water or glass.

**regardless** (ri gärd´ lis) *adv.* Without concern for.

**rein in** (rān´ in´) *v.* To stop a horse by pulling the reins.

**relieve** (ri lēv´) *v.* To comfort.

**reputation** (rep´ yə tā´ shən) *n.* The public's opinion of a person.

**resemble** (ri zem´ bəl) *v.* To be like.

**resist** (ri zist´) *v.* To struggle against; to oppose.

**respond** (ri spond´) *v.* To answer.

**restore** (ri stor´) *v.* To change something back to the way it used to be.

**rhubarb** (rōō´ bärb) *n.* A plant with green or red stalks that taste sharp or sour. Rhubarb is often cooked in pies.

**rogue** (rōg) *n.* A person who is not honest; a rascal.

**rolling pin** (rō´ ling pin´) *n.* A cylinder with handles, used to roll dough flat.

**rouse** (rouz) *v.* To wake up.

**safekeeping** (sāf´ kē´ ping) *n.* The act of protecting something.

**sagebrush** (sāj´ brush´) *n.* A grayish-green shrub that grows in the dry West.

**satisfy** (sat´ is fī´) *v.* To fill a need.

**scenery** (sē´ nə rē) *n.* The painted pictures and objects used on stage in a play.

**scope** (skōp) *n.* The amount of space.

**scrawl** (skrôl) *v.* To write in a fast, messy way. —*n.* A scribble.

**sculpt** (skulpt) *v.* To make a figure, statue, or design by carving wood or stone or by forming clay.

**sculpture** (skulp´ chər) *n.* A figure, statue, or design carved out of something solid.

**segregation** (seg´ ri gā´ shən) *n.* Keeping different races of people apart from each other.

**seize** (sēz) *v.* To grasp; to grab.

**selfish** (sel´ fish) *adj.* Caring only about oneself; not caring about others.

**serenade** (ser´ ə nād´) *n.* Music sung to someone.

**sesame** (ses´ə mē) *n.* The seed of an Asian plant, which is used to add flavor to food.

**severe** (sə vēr´) *adj.* Stern; strict; extremely harsh.

**shaft** (shaft) *n.* A ray or beam.

**sharp** (shärp) *n.* A musical note that sounds one-half tone higher than it usually does. —*adj.* 1. Clear. 2. Alert.

**shear** (shēr) *v.* To clip; to cut.

**shock** (shok) *v.* To surprise and upset at the same time.

**shutter** (shut´ ər) *n.* A doorlike cover that opens and closes over a window.

283 🐢

shutter

**sincere** (sin sēr´) *adj.* Honest.

**skillet** (skil´ it) *n.* A frying pan.

**Pronunciation Key:** at; lāte; câre;
fäther; set; mē; it; kīte; ox; rōse; ô in
bought; coin; boŏk; tōo; form; out; up;
tûrn; ə sound in about, chicken, pencil,
cannon, circus; chair; hw in which;
ring; shop; thin; there; zh in treasure.

**slump** (slump) *v.* To collapse; to sink
down.

**somma** (sum´ ə) *pron., prep.* The
words "some of" spoken together
rapidly.

**soothe** (sooth) *v.* To comfort.

**sought** (sôt) *v.* Past tense of **seek**: To
look for.

**spade** (spād) *n.* A digging tool with a
flat blade and a long handle.

**spake** (spāk) *v.* An old-fashioned past
tense of **speak**: To talk.

**splendor** (splen´ dər) *n.* Grandness;
magnificence.

**splinter** (splin´ tər) *n.* A small sharp
piece of wood broken off from a
larger piece.

**squeegee** (skwē´ jē) *v.* To make a
squeaking sound by rubbing as if
using a squeegee, which is a rubber-
edged tool for removing excess water
from windows.

**squiggle** (skwig´ əl) *n.* A line that is
curved or wavy.

**squirm** (skwûrm) *v.* To wriggle.

**starve** (stärv) *v.* To die from hunger.

284

**statue** (stach´ oo) *n.* A carved figure of
a person or an animal.

**sternly** (stûrn´ lē) *adv.* In a strict or
harsh way.

**stoop** (stoop) *n.* A small porch.

**strongbox** (strông´ boks´) *n.* A sturdy
box with a lock, for holding money or
other valuable items.

**stucco** (stuk´ ō) *n.* Plaster that covers
outside walls.

**style** (stīl) *n.* The way something is
done.

**suggestion** (səg jes´ chən) *n.* An idea;
advice.

**suitable** (soo´ tə bəl) *adj.* Fitting; right.

**surpass** (sər pas´) *v.* To be better than.

**suspicion** (sə spish´ ən) *n.* An idea
that something is wrong, but without
proof.

**tailor** (tā´ lər) *n.* A person who makes
clothing.

**taunt** (tônt) *n.* Spoken words that
make fun of someone in a mean way.

**terrace** (ter´ əs) *n.* A balcony; an
outdoor platform next to an
apartment.

**terror** (ter´ ər) *n.* Great fear.

**thresh** (thresh) *v.* To throw oneself
about wildly; to thrash.

**thus** (ᵺus) *adv.* In this way.

**token** (tō′ kən) *n.* A piece of metal shaped like a coin, used instead of money.

**traitor** (trā′ tər) *n.* A person who is not loyal to his or her country.

**trance** (trans) *n.* A state of not being fully conscious.

**treachery** (trech′ ə rē) *n.* Betrayal; trickery.

**trill** (tril) *v.* To make a vibrating sound, like the sound some birds make.

**trundle bed** (trun′ dl bed′) *n.* A low bed that stays under another bed when not in use.

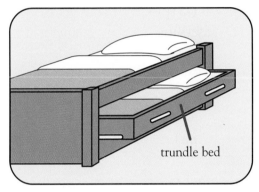

trundle bed

**turn** (tûrn) *v.* To repair a piece of clothing so that the side of the cloth that faced in now faces out.

**turpentine** (tûr′ pən tīn′) *n.* An oil used to thin paint.

**tusk** (tusk) *n.* A long, curving tooth or fang.

**twirl** (twûrl) *v.* To spin around.

**tyrant** (tī′ rənt) *n.* A cruel ruler.

**untangle** (un tang′ gəl) *v.* To remove tangles or knots.

**vanish** (van′ ish) *v.* To disappear.

**vigilante** (vij′ ə lan′ tē) *n.* A person who acts as if he or she is the law.

**violently** (vī′ ə lənt lē) *adv.* With destructive force.

**volunteer** (vol′ ən tēr′) *v.* To offer to do something.

285

**wart hog** (wort′ hôg′) *n.* An African wild pig.

**weary** (wēr′ ē) *adj.* Very tired; exhausted.

**whine** (hwīn) *v.* To talk in a complaining, annoying voice.

**widow** (wid′ ō) *n.* A woman whose husband has died.

**willies** (wil′ ēz) *n. pl.* A nervous fear.

**windowsill** (win′ dō sil′) *n.* The flat piece of wood at the bottom of a window.

**wondrous** (wun′ drəs) *adj.* Rare; surprising.

*continued from page 5*



**Photography**

195 UPI/Bettman
243 Sigrid Estrada

COLOPHON

*This book has been designed in the classic
style to emphasize our commitment to classic
literature. The typeface, Goudy Old Style, was
drawn in 1915 by Frederic W. Goudy, who based
it on fifteenth-century Italian letterforms.*

*The art has been drawn to reflect the golden age
of children's book illustration and its recent rebirth
in the work of innovative artists of today.
This book was designed by John Grandits.
Composition, electronic page makeup, and photo
and art management were provided by
The Chestnut House Group, Inc.*